Guide to
Marine Life
of British Columbia
by G. C. Carl

Columbia Provincial Museum

Canada

Carl

Guide to marine life in
British Columbia

BRITISH COLUMBIA PROVINCIAL MUSEUM

HANDBOOK No. 21

Date Due

British Columbia Cataloguing in Publication Data

Carl, George Clifford, 1908-1970.
    Guide to marine life of British Columbia.

    (British Columbia Provincial Museum.
Handbook ; no. 21)
    Bibliography: p.
    ISBN 0-7718-8012-X

1. Marine biology - British Columbia.
I. Title. II. Series.

QH95.3.C3   574.92'6'633   72-185930

Published by the British Columbia Provincial Museum,
Victoria.

First Printing - - - - - - 1963
Second Printing - - - - - 1966
Third Printing - - - - - - 1971
Fourth Printing - - - - - 1973
Fifth Printing - - - - - - 1978

Printed by K. M. MacDonald, Printer to the Queen's Most Excellent Majesty
in right of the Province of British Columbia.

PREFACE

The development of the plastic hull and dependable powerful outboard motors plus greater family income and leisure time have resulted in an increased interest in the sea as a recreational area. More persons than ever before are spending significant portions of their lives in and around boats and are finding pleasure in the out-of-doors along our coast-line. They are discovering new interests in natural history and are looking for sources of information about the plants and animals which come to their attention.

Fine reference books, such as " Between Pacific Tides," by Ricketts and Calvin, " Seashore Animals of the Pacific Coast," by Johnson and Snook, "Animals of the Seashore," by Guberlet, and " Common Seashore Life of the Pacific Northwest," by Smith, are available in libraries and occasionally in book-shops but a simplified introductory guide is lacking. This current number in the Handbook series is the result of an attempt to fill this need.

Because this booklet is intended to be used only as a guide and is designed particularly for use by the " boating fraternity," a relatively few plants and animals have been chosen to represent the vast number that actually exists. In most cases those that have been selected for inclusion are the conspicuous ones or are considered representative of the major groups. Many species that perhaps merit inclusion have been omitted to keep the booklet to a reasonable size. At the end of each section, references are given to enable the reader to pursue the topic further if desired.

The present publication contains very little that is new. Some of the material was taken from the works listed and some from earlier issues in the Handbook series or from other similar sources. I am indebted to the authors of these various references and also to members of the Museum staff who have helped in the preparation of the manuscript in several ways. I am also grateful to Dr. A. R. Fontaine and Mr. B. G. Howland, both of Victoria, and the British Columbia Government Travel Bureau for illustrative material, and to the Geographic Division of the Lands, Forests, and Water Resources Department for the chart of the coast-line.

G. C. C.

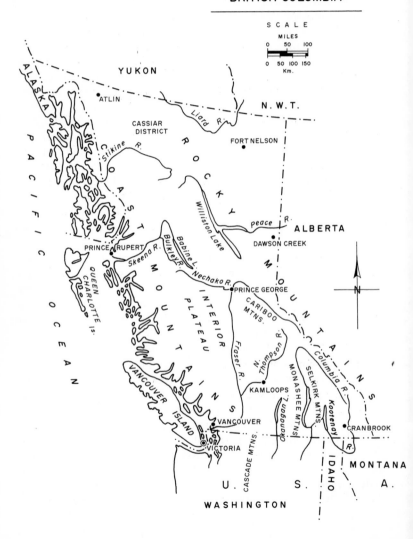

PROVINCE OF
BRITISH COLUMBIA

SCALE
MILES
0   50   100

0 50 100 150
Km.

YUKON

N.W.T.

ALASKA

ATLIN

CASSIAR
DISTRICT

Liard R.

FORT NELSON

PACIFIC

Stikine R.

ROCKY

Williston Lake

peace R.

ALBERTA

DAWSON CREEK

PRINCE RUPERT

Skeena R.

Babine L.

Bulkley R.

Nechako R.

PRINCE GEORGE

QUEEN
CHARLOTTE Is.

M
O
U
N
T
A
I
N
S

INTERIOR
PLATEAU

CARIBOO
MTNS.

Fraser R.

N. Thompson R.

M
O
U
N
T
A
I
N
S

N

OCEAN

VANCOUVER ISLAND

KAMLOOPS

Okanagan L.

MONASHEE MTNS.

SELKIRK MTNS.

Columbia R.

VANCOUVER

VICTORIA

CASCADE MTNS.

Kootenay R.

CRANBROOK

U.   S.   A.

IDAHO

MONTANA

WASHINGTON

CONTENTS

Guide to Marine Life of British Columbia

INTRODUCTION

Being a creature of dry land, man has a somewhat biased opinion of the relative importance of the land and of the ocean. To him the continents and islands which make up the habitable parts of the globe and the animals and plants which live upon these land masses are of prime importance. However, from the standpoint of area occupied by the sea and also the numbers of individual living things found therein, the land and its life have to take second place. Less than one-third of the earth's surface is above water, and all land creatures put together are greatly out-numbered by the swarming life of the sea.

The crust of the earth is far from being smooth; it is thrown into folds we call mountains or depresssed to form ocean depths. Yet if the surface were smoothed—that is, if the mountain ranges and the great land-masses were levelled down and the ocean bottoms raised to the same elevation—water would cover the entire surface to a uniform depth of about 2¼ miles.

Although the oceans of the world are much greater in extent than the land-masses, the total amount of water in relation to the earth's mass is really very small. A graphic method of picturing this relationship is to visualize the world as a ball 3 feet in diameter. If such a sphere is dipped into water and removed, the resulting film of moisture clinging to its surface would represent the quantity of water in all the oceans in relation to the mass of the earth.

SALINITY

This film of moisture which we call the sea nevertheless presents a unique set of conditions which makes it possible for a vast assemblage of living creatures, both plants and animals, to find a home. While these conditions of life are often complex and interdependent, a few of them are relatively simple and yet fundamental. The most important factor influencing marine forms, and certainly the most obvious one, is the presence of salt in the water. It is more correct to say " salts " however, because in addition to common salt there are many different substances present, several of which are technically known as salts.

The major components are sodium chloride (common salt), magnesium chloride, magnesium sulphate, and calcium sulphate in varying concentrations, but in unvarying proportions. Compounds containing potassium, bromine, iodine, and other elements are also present. In fact, most known elements are to be found in the sea, but, of course, some are in very small quantities.

The amount of dissolved material in sea-water varies slightly in different parts of the ocean and particularly in inshore waters, where dilution occurs by mixing with river-water, but on the average it ranges between 3.0 and 3.5 per cent of the water by weight. In other words, every 100 pounds of sea-water (9½ imperial gallons) contains about 3½ pounds of dissolved materials.

The importance of all these elements in sea-water as far as living organisms are concerned is fairly obvious since many of these substances are necessary for life, growth, and reproduction. Marine creatures, as it were, are bathed in life-giving elements; they have only to absorb those required. This may partly explain why life originated in the sea (as it is now fairly generally believed) and also why living things are so abundant in the sea. However, since the demand for some of these dissolved substances, such as the phosphates, is greater than for others, these materials are often partially depleted in areas where rapid growth or multiplication has occurred, in which case the short supply acts as a natural check on reproduction. Seasonal death of marine organisms again releases these critical substances for further use; fresh supplies are also brought in by tidal and other movements of water from the deeper waters lying off the coast.

There are two major theories regarding the origin of the salts in the sea. The first supposes that they have been carried into the ocean by rain-water dissolving out material from the soil and flowing into the sea via the earth's river systems. Certainly huge quantities of dissolved materials as well as suspended, undissolved materials are carried into the sea every year by all the rivers of the world, but not enough to account for the immense amounts now found in ocean-water.

A more acceptable theory postulates that marine elements have originated by volcanic action. During the earth's early history great eruptions poured forth huge quantities of materials, part of which become dissolved in the water condensing on the earth's surface, thus forming the early seas. Material is still being added at a great rate, aided to a considerable extent by man's activities, but nothing like the rate during this eruptive phase in the earth's history.

From the standpoint of supply, sea-water is ideally suited for the support of living things. Water, most necessary for life, is in unlimited quantity, and the chemicals necessary to build protoplasm are present in immediately available form and in almost any required amount. Thus, with respect to availability of building materials, the ocean is almost a perfect living-place for both plants and animals.

TEMPERATURE

In the marine world, as on land, temperature plays a vital role. On land in some places we experience temperature ranges of considerable magnitude, say from 30° or 40° below zero in winter to more than 100° F. in the shade during the summer. In the sea, however, the maximum range possible is from 28.5° F. (3.5° below freezing at great depths) to about 92° F. near the surface in parts of the tropics.

In the region of Victoria on Vancouver Island the range between winter and summer in the upper layers is about 46° to 54° as indicated by records taken at the Quarantine Station at William Head. In more protected waters, such as are found along the east coast of Vancouver Island, the annual range is from about 42° to 64°, a yearly fluctuation of 22°. Generally speaking, however, the temperature of the open sea is below 60° F. and seldom lower than 45°.

Fishes and other creatures living in the open sea, therefore, are not called upon to tolerate very wide ranges in temperature. Their

11

environment is relatively uniform in this regard; they enjoy an equitable climate.

However, the temperature conditions are greatly different along the seashore. Here the range is considerably influenced by the weather; consequently, on a wintry night at low tide, freezing conditions may exist and on a hot summer's day the first flow of water from the returning tide may be well over 80° F. Plants and animals exposed to these extremes are sometimes harmed or killed; those which persist must be tolerant to fairly wide temperature changes.

Several species of fish, crabs, seaweeds, and other organisms are regularly found in tide pools. These obviously must also be capable of standing high temperatures and other unfavourable conditions found in trapped water.

CURRENTS

Largely as a result of forces exerted by prevailing winds, there are great movements of ocean-water called " drifts " or " ocean currents." The Gulf Stream and Labrador Current of the Atlantic are familiar examples. In the North-east Pacific we have the West Wind Drift or so-called " Japanese Current," which sweeps westward at a leisurely 2 to 3 knots to divide about 400 miles off the Vancouver Island coast. Part turns north to become dissipated in the Gulf of Alaska; the remainder turns south along the coast of California. The point of division, hence the path followed, and the rate of flow all vary from season to season, so that the pattern of circulation is always changing and often complex.

This great flow of warm water is largely responsible for the moderate, damp climate of the coastal area, and it also accounts for the periodic appearance of southern fishes such as the albacore (tuna), ocean sunfish, baracuda, and pompano.

Close to shore another band of water flows slowly northward along the British Columbia and Alaska coast, finally to lose itself in the Bering Sea area. This narrow coastal current is a mixture of river-water and sea-water forming a cold brackish layer quite distinct from the warmer water offshore. It is mostly responsible for the fog banks which form along the coastline at certain seasons.

These currents of warm and cold water have considerable influence on the movements of fishes along the coast. For example, in 1958 the volume of warm water flowing north was greatly increased, with the result that the temperature of the sea off the west coast of Vancouver Island was considerably higher than usual. Consequently, when the sockeye salmon moved southward to the Fraser River, they chose a route through the cooler waters of Johnstone Strait on the east coast of Vancouver Island instead of the normal route along the west coast and through Juan de Fuca Strait. As a result, the value of the Canadian catch was increased by about $6,000,000.

TIDES

Because of the attractive forces of the moon and sun, the water-masses which make up the oceans are influenced in such a way as to produce movements we call " tides." The pattern and rhythm of these movements are very regular in the open sea, but along our irregular coast-line they vary tremendously from place to place in a complicated manner. A detailed explanation of these tidal forces is given in the introduction to the Pacific Coast Tide and Current Tables published by the Federal Government for each year.

In general terms it may be said that along the southern section of the British Columbia coastline, levels may vary from a foot or so below zero (a minus tide) to 12 or 15 feet above zero; farther north, high tides reach a maximum of 24 feet. Along most of the outer coast north from Juan de Fuca Strait there are two sets of tides each day, but at the southern end of Vancouver Island and along adjacent shorelines only one set of daily tides is experienced.

Twice each month, two to three days after new and full moon, the tides reach their highest levels; these are popularly called " spring tides," and the series of lower high tides that occur in the intervals are called " neap tides."

Because of these periodic changes in water-level, great quantities of water flow along the coast and through the channels, first in one direction then in the opposite direction. These tidal currents have a great influence on inshore fishes since they carry food and fresh water from one point to another. So important are these currents that the feeding activities of many fish species are geared to

13

the same rhythm of water movements, and anglers find it profitable to " fish the tides." Current conditions differ in each locality, but, in general, increased feeding activities of fishes occur around low slack and high slack periods, and when these times coincide with dawn or dusk, catches are at their highest.

UP-WELLINGS

There is another movement of water along our coastline which is less obvious but probably most important so far as marine life is concerned. This is a movement of relatively cold water from the deeper parts of the ocean into the straits and inshore waters to compensate for the fresher (and lighter) surface water which flows away from the coast. This oceanic water is of great importance because it carries with it substances such as phosphates and nitrates which are in short supply in areas where living creatures abound. " Up-wellings " of these life-giving waters are aided in local waters by the run-off of the Fraser River; major effects may be noted near the western entrance to Active Pass, for example, where Fraser water and ocean-water mixes. Here tremendous crops of " plankton " are produced in spring and early summer; the myriads of minute plants and animals colour the water for miles and provide food for many fishes and other larger forms of life, even including whales.

TYPES OF SHORE

Where the sea meets the land, several types of beaches are found, the type depending mainly upon the kind of material exposed to the water and upon the amount of protection it receives. Thus we find at least four kinds of beaches along our shorelines—rock, boulder, sand, and mud. Often two or more types will be closely associated, as when boulders or sand are exposed at the base of a rock bluff or a rocky promontory marks the limit of a sand or mud beach. In any case, since living conditions vary markedly in these four types of habitats, we find that each supports a characteristic marine community of plants and animals, including fishes.

Rock.—On the rocky type of shore, living creatures are found only in the cracks and crannies where it is possible for them to get a " foothold " and at the same time to escape from the direct effect of the surf. Bladder wrack, sea-lettuce, and many of the " mossy " types of seaweed find anchorage here. Among the animals, barnacles, mussels, limpets, chitons, and fan-like colonies of moss-animals are present, each one with its own peculiar type of shell for protection. Concavities in the rock which trap the receding waters may shelter other forms, including hermit crabs, oyster drills, sea-urchins, and other creatures which cannot live out of water for any length of time. All are provided with some means of securing themselves to the rock, either by root-like " hold-fasts " in the case of the plants or by a sucker-like foot, strong threads, cement, or claws in the case of the various animals.

Fishes common to the rocky shore include the rockfishes, greenlings, lingcod, seaperches, coho and spring salmon. Some of these are here because they feed upon animals and plants found on the rock face, while others, like the salmon, are possibly attracted by the presence of herring and other food-fishes.

Boulders.—Boulders offer more protection than rock, especially where cavities exist beneath the masses of stone. Here a greater variety of shore forms take up their abode, some permanently, some only at certain seasons. Among permanent residents may be found shore crabs, barnacles, various tube worms, certain chitons, and occasional sponges. Fishes are represented by the clingfish, which attaches itself by an abdominal sucker, blennies, and various sculpins.

Temporary inhabitants are young stages of the red rock crab, spawning whelks or oyster drills, and male singing-fish guarding masses of pea-sized eggs attached to a rock ceiling.

Sand.—On sandy shores the inhabitants must be specialized for living in a shifting medium. Only a few kinds of plants are found, mainly eel-grass, which is anchored by well-developed roots; the animals are mostly burrowing forms with special equipment for " digging in."

Among the fishes, the most interesting is perhaps the sandlance, which buries itself with only the head projecting above the surface. Here, too, are several species of flounders, halibut, and other flatfishes, which merge so well with the background they are practically

15

invisible. Some of the seaperches are also found here, feeding over the surface of the sand or in the eel-grass beds.

Mud.—In mud habitats, usually at the heads of long bays and inlets or around estuaries, living conditions are much more stable. Abundant basic food is available in the form of detritus and other decaying material which settles out from the relatively quiet water. Here molluscs, worms, and other small forms which feed directly upon this food are, in turn, food for larger species, including fishes.

Fishes likely to be found in shallow water over a muddy bottom include flounders, sculpins, skates, and occasionally dogfish. In burrows formed by mud shrimps and ghost shrimps, the arrow goby is almost sure to be present, and in deeper water ratfishes, skates, sea-poachers, eelpouts, and species with similar habits are likely to be taken.

Most commercial trawling is done on a sand or a hard mud bottom, which is less likely to damage a net, and the catch usually includes the above-mentioned fishes plus soles, tomcod, Pacific cod, and occasionally rockfish.

SEAWEEDS

Most of the marine plants which we call "seaweeds" belong to the algæ, a group within the plant kingdom. The algæ include a great variety of plant forms which are simple in their cellular structure but which may be complex in their outward appearance. In fact, many members of this group are exceedingly difficult to identify even by specialists.

A few seaweeds, for example the eel-grasses, are not algæ, but are composed of true roots, stems, and leaves, and are therefore members of the highest plant division, the Spermatophytes. They are the only truly marine vascular plants and are an important source of food for many waterfowl.

Kelp; Bull Kelp;   *Nereocystis luetkeana*
Ribbon Kelp   **(Mertens) Postels and Ruprecht**

A plant with a long stalk anchored to the bottom and expanding into a bulb at the top end. Two pairs of long leaf-like fronds spring from the bulb. The upper portion of the stem and the bulb are hollow, acting as a float. The lower end is attached by a root-like "holdfast." Colour of entire plant golden brown to dark brown. Total length from 50 to 100 feet.

Kelp is so distinctive in its appearance that once seen it is easily recognized and remembered. It has a wide distribution, being found in its various forms along the shores of most continents. Our local species ranges from California to Alaska and along the shores of the Western Pacific as well.

It grows on rocky bottom in water varying in depth between 5 and 50 feet. In favourable places, beds many acres in extent may occur.

Despite its large size, kelp is an alga, the plant group to which the smallest and least specialized plants belong. Most algæ are microscopic in size.

Kelp is a " friend " to the boater. It marks dangerous shoals, rocks, and reefs. It indicates the direction and approximate speed of currents by its action in the water. It provides an attractive habitat for food and game fishes. It acts as a temporary anchor for small craft. And finally it adds an interesting tidbit to the menu for it can be eaten! (*See* Appendix.)

Kelp is an annual; that is, most of the plants die off at the end of a year and are later replaced by new growth. As in the case of many of the so-called " lower " plants, spores are produced in the fall. These swim free for a while then settle to produce the beginnings of a new plant. Only those in the most suitable habitat succeed in growing to maturity. Growth is necessarily rapid, sometimes as much as 2 inches a day.

A related species, giant kelp (*Macrocystis*), differs in having a series of small floats, each on the end of a short side-branch. This kelp is found on the west coast of Vancouver Island and along other shorelines exposed to ocean conditions. Individual plants with stalks over 100 feet in length have been measured.

Indians made use of kelp in several ways. The solid portions of the stalk were cured and knotted together to form rope or fishline, which is surprisingly serviceable so long as it is kept oiled and not immersed for long periods. The hollow stem was said to be used as a speaking-tube during dance ceremonies, and the bulb was occasionally used as a storage receptacle for eulachon oil.

Bladder Wrack; Rockweed; Popping Wrack

Fucus furcatus C. Agardh.

A much-branching flattened seaweed, each branch with a swollen tip. Branches in pairs (dichotomous) commencing with a single rounded stalk attached to rock or pile. Colour greenish-brown to dark brown. Length to 12 inches.

Bladder wrack is a very common seaweed characteristic of the beachline between low- and high-tide levels. It is capable of withstanding exposure even on hot summer days; in fact, it seems to thrive best high on the beach where it is exposed even at half-tides.

The bladders on the ends of the finger-like branchlets act as floats to buoy up the plant in the water. In addition to a bubble of gas, they contain a mucilaginous material plus sea-water, which squirts out through minute holes when the plant is squeezed.

Reproduction is by eggs and sperms produced in pits dotting the surface of each mature bulb. The eggs become fertilized after being discharged into the water, and the developing plant eventually settles and becomes attached. Reproduction takes place at all seasons.

Bladder wrack is found from Alaska to central California. Along some beaches it is the most abundant seaweed.

A long, soft, flexible much-branched plant with many small bladder-like floats. The main stem arises from an attached conical disk, and at more or less regular intervals side-branches are given off alternately. To these are attached long flexible secondary branches, which give rise to numerous leaf-like structures and also to small bulbs which act as floats. Bulbs are single and not pointed at the apex. General colour dark brown. Total length 4 to 6 feet.

Jap-weed is notorious because it frequently becomes a pest to anglers and sometimes to boaters in general. Detached portions of the weed floating free in the water get snagged on fishing-gear, forcing the fisherman to constantly clear his lines or to abandon the area completely. It also becomes picked up by propellers, sometimes to such an extent it becomes necessary to stop the motor and spend some time with gaff or boat hook in disentangling the twisted mass of weed.

Jap-weed apparently was introduced into British Columbia along with Japanese oysters about 1944, but for a number of years it was unrecognized because it resembles very closely a similar seaweed, *Cystoseira*. The latter can be distinguished by the bladders which are sometimes in pairs and *always pointed* at the apex.

A long-bladed grass-like plant usually growing in large beds. Each plant a group of three to six leaves, originating from a common root-stalk. At maturity greenish-coloured flowers are produced, arranged alternately on the mid-rib of a leaf-like spike. Colour of the leaves dull green; stalk light green. Length up to 10 feet or more.

Eel-grass is not truly a " seaweed " since it is a land plant that blooms under water; fertilization is effected by thread-like pollen carried by water instead of by air or insects as in the case of most land plants. The seed is nut-like.

Eel-grass is the favourite food of black brant and other sea-birds as well as of many marine animals. It is the favourite haunt of commercial crabs and of both young and adults of many food-fishes. It is also widely used as spawning-beds by various fishes, molluscs, and other marine forms.

It commonly grows in mud or mud mixed with sand, just below the low-tide level, and is found from Alaska to California.

A related form called " false eel-grass " (*Phyllospadix*) is found growing on rocks exposed at low tide. The leaves of this species are bright emerald green in colour and quite narrow.

REFERENCES

Guberlet, Muriel L. 1956. Seaweeds at Ebb Tide. Univ. of Wash. Press, Seattle, pp. 1–182.

Scagel, Robert F. 1948. An Investigation on Marine Plants near Hardy Bay, B.C., with Particular Reference to Certain Marine Algæ (Seaweeds), Their Methods of Growth, Effects of Harvesting and Conservation. Report No. 1, B.C. Dept. of Fisheries, pp. 1–70.

Scagel, Robert F. 1956. Introduction of a Japanese Alga, *Sargassum muticum,* into the Northeast Pacific. Fish. Res. Papers, Washington Dept. Fish., 1 (4), pp. 49–58.

Scagel, Robert F. 1957. An Annotated List of the Marine Algæ of British Columbia and Northern Washington (including keys to genera). Bull. No. 150, National Museum, Ottawa, pp. 289.

Scagel, Robert F. 1961. Marine Plant Resources of British Columbia. Fish. Res. Bd., Canada, Bull. 127, pp. 1–39.

Smith, Gilbert M. 1944. Marine Algæ of the Monterey Peninsula, California. Stanford University Press.

MAMMALS

Mammals are not particularly abundant in the sea, but when they do appear they are likely to be spectacular, as in the case of whales. These and the other specialized forms, such as the porpoises, seals, and sea-lions, always attract attention when sighted.

Like all mammals, these marine species are warm-blooded, they breathe air, and give birth to living young which are suckled. To protect themselves from the cold, some have a covering of water-repellent hair or hair and fur, some have a coat of blubber as well, and others have blubber only. To permit long dives, all are able to hold their breath for extended periods of time.

The river otter, mink, and raccoon are included in this section because they may be sighted along the shore and occasionally in the water in the case of the otter and the mink.

Killer Whale   *Orcinus rectipinna* **(Cope)**

A large porpoise-like whale with a prominent back fin and conspicuous white markings. Length probably to 26 feet in males and

20 feet in females. Colour black with white on the throat and belly extending well up the flank on each side; a white oval-shaped patch behind each eye and a whitish saddle behind the back fin in males. Back fin very long and straight in mature males; shorter and curved in females and juveniles.

Killer whales may be sighted anywhere along the coast or in the open water sometimes far from land. They are particularly common around the Gulf Islands, including the San Juan group in Washington, in Puget Sound, in Juan de Fuca Strait, and off the mouth of the Fraser. · They travel in groups numbering from two or three individuals up to 100 or more, and they are always " on the move." Killer whales pass East Point, Saturna Island, more or less regularly once or twice a week in summer, less frequently in winter, according to light-station attendants.

Like other members of the porpoise family, killers usually rise three or more times in succession to blow before sounding. Each roll takes from three to five seconds, and the interval between rolls varies from six to ten seconds, after which the animal may stay submerged for many minutes. Occasionally killers leap clear of the water, stand on their tails, flap the tail vigorously on the surface, or perform other gymnastic feats. The sound of the blowing is a rather explosive puff, which may carry some distance over the water under favourable conditions. The spout, though rarely visible, may rise 5 to 7 feet, some say 15 to 20 feet on a windless day.

Killers are armed with ten to thirteen pairs of conical teeth in each jaw, arranged so they interlock. Food consists of anything " catchable," such as seals, sea-lions, porpoises, various fishes, squids, and sea-birds. They also attack larger whales which have no effective defence against " wolf pack " tactics. There are no authentic records of them attacking humans, but it would be wise not to provide them with an opportunity.

Harbour Porpoise   *Phocœna vomerina* **Gill**

A small dark-coloured porpoise with a low back fin. Length up to 6 feet and weight to 160 pounds. Colour dark grey or black on the back, light grey or nearly white on the undersurface. A dark stripe from corner of the mouth to origin of flipper.

The harbour porpoise is the species most commonly seen along inshore waters and up to 20 miles off shore. It is usually easily distinguished by its small size, low fin, and dark colour with no white showing on the sides above the water-line. It usually travels in small groups of two to four individuals and is rather shy and timid. Only rarely does it surface near a boat, and it never plays about the bows of a travelling ship. Ordinarily, all one sees is a small portion of the back and the low dorsal fin as the animal rises at the surface to breathe. The movement is best described as a "roll" and takes about two seconds to complete. As a rule each animal rolls three or four times at intervals of several seconds before sounding and may not appear again for several minutes. In quiet waters and when the porpoise is relatively close, the blowing can be heard as a soft "puff." The puff is made by a short exhalation followed immediately by a longer inhalation, sounding like " huf-uhhh."

The jaws of the harbour porpoise are armed with twenty-four or twenty-five spade-shaped teeth on each side. Food is herring and other small fishes plus squid. Harbour porpoises may dive to a depth of at least 44 fathoms. Mating occurs in July to October, and a single young, about 2 feet long, is produced after a gestation period of 183 days.

Dall Porpoise   *Phocœnoides dalli* (True)

A dark heavy-set porpoise with white on the sides. Length up to 6 feet and weight about 250 pounds. Colour dull blue-black with a large white patch across the belly and extending well up on each side. The back fin is frequently tipped with white. A prominent hump on the back just forward of the flukes.

The Dall porpoise occurs along the entire coast of British Columbia and some distance off shore, but it is essentially northern in its distribution. Occasionally small schools are seen around the Gulf Islands, but it is by no means common in this area.

Unlike the harbour porpoise, this species delights in playing about the bow of a moving ship. Six to twenty or more may accompany a boat, dashing back and forth across the bow and occasionally breaking the surface to breath. They are capable of travelling at a speed of at least 12 knots.

When leisurely rising to blow, the Dall porpoise arches its back more sharply than does the harbour porpoise and the back fin is more prominent. Like its cousin, it feeds on herring and other small fishes.

Humpback Whale   *Megaptera novœangliœ* (Borowski)

A large stout-bodied whale with a hump-like dorsal fin. Length up to 50 feet. Almost entirely black in colour, underparts of flukes and flippers usually white. Flippers long and narrow with many irregular knobs along the leading edge. Barnacles usually on snout, chin, and lower jaw. About twenty-six widely spaced grooves on throat and chest.

The humpback is the only large whale regularly seen along the coastline, where it frequently enters partially enclosed straits and inlets. It may be recognized by its size, and by its spout, which is low and bushy, arising as twin columns of vapour and expanding into a " mushroom." Another recognition feature is the habit of lifting the flukes clear of the water when sounding.

Courting males may leap free of the water or roll at the surface with one flipper splashing vigorously.

The breeding period is mainly in the winter months; one young is born at a time, with an average length of about 16 feet. Food is almost entirely " red feed " (small shrimp-like creatures called " euphausids "), but small fishes are probably also taken. A 45-foot individual was found to weigh 32 tons.

Humpback whales range from the Arctic Ocean and Bering Sea south to the waters off Central America.

Sharp-nosed Finner; Minke; Pike Whale

Balænoptera acutorostrata **Lacepede**

A small, slender, torpedo-shaped whale with a low, curved back fin. Maximum length 30 feet; local individuals seldom exceed 24 feet in length. Colour black on the back and white on the under-surfaces. A conspicuous white band crosses each flipper. Throat and belly with many grooves extending back to umbilicus.

This is the small whale most commonly seen along the coast-line and particularly among the Gulf Islands. It may be recognized by its size (larger than a porpoise, smaller than other whales) and by its back fin (much smaller and more curved than that of a killer whale). Very seldom is more than one individual seen in any one area, and often a lone whale frequents an area for extended periods of time. Food consists of herring, sand lance, and other small fishes.

When surfacing, usually the top of the head and the back with its small curved fin are visible for two or three seconds. The blow is scarcely visible, and the fluke (tail fin) is not lifted clear of the surface before diving. Occasionally a frisky individual will leap completely out of the water, two or three times in succession like a gigantic salmon, and occasionally one will rise to blow alongside a travelling yacht, much to the surprise of skipper and crew.

Other names for this small whale are sharp-headed finner, lesser rorqual, and Davidson's whale. It is found from the Arctic Ocean south to Baja, California, but is not taken by whalers because of its comparatively small size.

The name " minke " came into use among Norwegian whalers in derision of a fellow whaler called Meinche who mistook a school of these whales for blue whales. (Budker, 1958.)

Hair Seal; Harbour Seal   *Phoca vitulina* Linnæus

A seal with a rounded, dog-like head; no external ears; eyes large and high on the head. Length up to 5½ feet and weight to 300 pounds. Hair coarse with no underfur. Fore flippers short, covered with hair, and ending in claws. Hind flippers incapable of being extended forward.

Colour usually marbled and blotched with dark markings on grey or almost white. Pups silvery-grey.

The hair seal is likely to be confused only with the sea-lion or with the fur seal, but it may be distinguished easily by its rounder head, larger eyes, and grey colour, and by the  lack of external ears. It also swims differently, sinking quietly backwards beneath the surface and never broaching or leaping as do the other types of seals. Propulsion is mainly by the hind flippers, not by the fore flippers as in sea-lions and fur seals. Hair seals are most usually seen close to shore in shallow bays and near river-mouths. They haul out on rocky reefs or sand-bars, taking up a position from which they can quickly wriggle and flop into the water when alarmed.

Food is largely coarse fish and crustaceans and occasionally octopus. They will take salmon and other commercially valuable fishes when opportunity permits, but this is infrequently.

Mating takes place in midsummer, but development of the embryo does not begin until a few weeks later. The gestation period is about nine months, and a single pup is born in late May or June. Birth takes place on isolated reefs or on bars in the mouth of a large river.

Not counting man, the hair seal's chief predator is the killer whale; when pursued by these mammals, hair seals seek refuge in shallow water and even haul out on the beach.

Northern Sea-lion   *Eumetopias jubata* **(Schreber)**

A large seal with a relatively small head, more elongate than in the hair seal; small external ears present. Length of males up to 11 feet and weight to 2,200 pounds; females about half as large. Fore flippers long and paddle-shaped with the edge extending beyond the claws. Hind flippers capable of being rotated forward and used in locomotion on land.

Colour more or less uniform tan or buff; young are dark brown.

The northern sea-lion may be distinguished from the hair seal by the head shape and the presence of external ears. The profile is characteristic too, giving the impression of an upturned nose when seen from the side. The tan colour is most distinctive.

The larger size, pale coloration, lack of crest on the head of adult males, and voice (a deep-throated bellow) serve to distinguish this species from the California sea-lion.

34

Sea-lions use the fore flippers for swimming, the hind flippers acting as stabilizers or rudders; the forequarters are consequently unusually heavy and well developed. In spite of its great bulk, a sea-lion is extremely graceful and swift in the water. When swimming, its neck and body appear to be unusually stretched out, creating an impression of serpentine motion, which has fooled many an observer into thinking he has seen a " sea-serpent."

Sea-lions may be seen almost anywhere along the coast from California to Alaska. In British Columbia they are particularly abundant around breeding areas such as the Scott Islands (northern Vancouver Island), Price Island, and Cape St. James (Queen Charlotte Islands). They feed upon lampreys, squid, sandlance, pollack, flounders, sculpins, cod, herring, small sharks, skates, perch, and various other scrap fish, with small amounts of salmon, halibut, and sablefish. Large numbers of eulachon are eaten when these fish are on their spawning migration.

Breeding takes place in June and July, at which time mature males gather harems of ten to twenty cows on the rookeries. Each female gives birth to one pup, which is suckled for about three months.

River Otter   *Lutra canadensis* (Schreber)

A long sinuous mammal with a broad, flat head, small ears, and small eyes. Males sometimes exceed 4 feet in total length and weigh up to 30 pounds. Legs short and muscular, all five toes fully webbed. Tail long and muscular, broad at the base and evenly tapered. Fur short and dense.

Colour uniform dark brown above, lighter below.

The otter is equally at home in water as on land; consequently, individuals may be seen swimming in bays and estuaries anywhere along the coastline. Ordinarily, when swimming, only the head is visible, but it may be distinguished from that of any of the seals by its smaller size, dark-brown colour, and ears shaped like those of a land animal.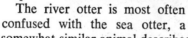

The river otter is most often confused with the sea otter, a somewhat similar animal described in the following section.

River otters live in dens, which are usually situated under tree roots or slabs of rock close to the water. The adjacent shoreline is often well marked with beaten trails and droppings containing fish bones and crab or mollusc shell.

In seashore habitats, otters feed mostly on crabs, but they also catch fish and an occasional bird. In Victoria harbour, mussels are removed from piles and eaten.

One to five young are born in March or April after a gestation period of about two months.

Frank L. Beebe
—1944—

Sea Otter   *Enhydra lutris* **(Linnæus)**

A mammal much like the river otter in size and appearance but very different in habits. Total length up to 5 feet and weight between 50 and 80 pounds.   Head broad and flat, with small ears and eyes.   Legs short and muscular;   the hind feet paddle-like, furred on both sides and with well-developed webs between the toes.   Tail thick and short (10 inches).   Fur dense and grizzled in appearance.

Colour dark brown to yellowish-grey, paler around the snout and shoulders.

The sea otter is almost entirely aquatic in its habit, hauling out only occasionally on weed-covered rocks.   It frequents kelp-beds and other rocky areas where sea-urchins are found in abundance. It habitually sleeps or swims on its back and is remarkably buoyant, so much so that the entire head, the fore flippers, and much of the belly and parts of the hind flippers ride above the surface.

The sea otter feeds primarily on sea-urchins and molluscs, which it gathers by diving.   Using the chest as a table, the otter lies on its back to eat and occasionally uses a stone on which to break the shells.

One young is born at a time in April or May.   The life-span is about eight years.

In the early days sea otters were found along the entire coast of British Columbia, and their skins formed one of the main incentives for traders in this area.   Now they are rare; occasional sight records indicate there may be a few individual animals in certain areas.   A small population exists in the Aleutian area, and representatives of a southern race occur along a part of the coast of southern California.

Mink *Mustela vison* **Schreber**

A small, dark, weasel-like animal, sinuous in its movements. Males up to 2 feet in length and 3 pounds in weight; females about half. Head flattened, the eye small and beady. Legs short and provided with five claws on each foot. Tail moderately long and bushy. Fur dense, fine, and glossy.

Colour dark brown with irregular patches of white on the throat and sometimes on other areas of the underparts.

The mink is usually seen close to water, often along the seashore or along banks of rivers, streams, and lakes.

It feeds mostly on crabs and other crustacea along the sea-beach, but it will also catch fish and birds.

Breeding takes place in March, and three to ten young are born in a litter about six weeks later, in cavities under rock or in burrows of other animals.

Mink.   Raccoon.

Raccoon   *Procyon lotor* (Linnæus)

A heavy-bodied animal not likely to be confused with any other. Total length about 3 feet, weight up to 22 pounds. Head sharp-pointed and with a prominent black mask around the eyes and over the cheek. Ears fairly prominent. Well-developed legs; toes with prominent claws. Tail long and bushy, marked with dark rings. Fur long and somewhat shaggy.

Colour grey over all; white on the face and feet. Mask and tail-rings black.

The raccoon is an omnivorous feeder and hence may be seen almost anywhere along the seashore, where it searches for crabs, molluscs, and stranded fishes. While it is largely nocturnal in habit, it may occasionally forage by day, particularly along unsettled areas. The footprints are commonly seen on sand and mud banks.

One to six young are born in the spring after a gestation period of about sixty-three days.

REFERENCES

Budker, Paul. 1958. Whales and Whaling. Geo. G. Harrap & Co. Ltd.

Carl, G. Clifford. 1946. Sharp-headed Finner Whale Stranded at Sidney, Vancouver Island, British Columbia. Murrelet, Vol. 27, No. 3, pp. 47–49.

Carl, G. Clifford. 1946. A School of Killer Whales Stranded at Estevan Point, Vancouver Island. Prov. Mus. Rept. for 1945, pp. 21–28.

Carl, G. Clifford. 1960. Albinistic Killer Whales in British Columbia. Prov. Mus. Rept. for 1959, pp. 29–36.

Cowan, Ian McT., and Guiguet, Charles J. 1960. The Mammals of British Columbia. B.C. Prov. Museum Handbook, No. 11, pp. 1–413.

Pike, Gordon C. 1956. Guide to the Whales, Porpoises and Dolphins of the North-east Pacific and Arctic Waters of Canada and Alaska. Circular No. 32, Fish. Res. Bd., Canada, Nanaimo, B.C., pp. 1–15.

Scheffer, Victor B., and Slipp, John W. 1948. The Whales and Dolphins of Washington State with a Key to the Cetaceans of the West Coast of North America. Amer. Mid. Nat. 39 (2), pp. 257–337.

BIRDS

The birds which spend part or all their life on the sea, or associated with it, represent many diverse groups. They range from the loons and grebes, which are almost entirely confined to water and are consequently helpless on land, to the eagle and some of the shorebirds that hunt along the beach but cannot or do not swim.

Most of the so-called sea-birds are adapted in some way for an aquatic life. All have plumage of a type that is resistant to water so that the bird is not only bouyant, but also well insulated from cold. All have either webs between the toes or paddle-like extension of the toes for efficient swimming, and most have other special adaptations which permit them to dive and remain submerged for extended periods of time.

The birds as a group are better known than any other group of animals connected with the sea. A number of good guides and other references concerning birds are available; a few are listed at the end of this section.

Loons

A large, heavy diving bird with a short tail and a dagger-like bill.

Three relatively common species are as follows:—

Common Loon.—The colour in winter is largely dull grey on the back, head, neck, and sides and with white on the underparts. Small V-shaped white specks are present on the back. In the summer, while breeding on fresh-water lakes, loons are greenish-black on the upper parts with a white " necklace " around the throat and white " checker-board " on the back. The underparts are silvery-white.

The common loon spends the winter months on salt water and occasionally on some of the larger lakes. In the spring those on the sea migrate to fresh water for nesting.

This bird is also known as the great northern diver or great northern loon. It is ordinarily a wary bird; when approached it slips beneath the surface in a characteristic rolling dive, swims rapidly under water to surface some distance away. It feeds upon fish, which it captures in direct under-water pursuit.

The loon is primarily adapted for living on water; consequently, its legs are placed far back on the body, making it an efficient swimmer but almost helpless on land. It is also a good strong flyer but requires a long flapping run over the surface of the water in order to become air-borne.

Arctic Loon.—Distinctly smaller than the common loon and similar in colour during the winter but lacking the white spots on the back.   In spring and summer the Arctic loon is also very similar to the common loon in appearance but is distinguished by having an ashy-grey patch extending from the forehead to the hind neck.

Arctic loons are most usually seen along the British Columbia coast during the spring and fall migration.

F. L. Beebe

Red-throated Loon.—About the same size as the Arctic loon but with the bill slightly upturned.

The red-throated loon is very similar in coloration to the Arctic loon in winter but has fine speckles on the back. In spring and summer the head and neck are slate-grey with a conspicuous maroon-red throat-patch. The back is an even greyish-brown, and the underparts are white.

Grebes

Small or medium-sized diving birds with a relatively long neck, a straight, pointed bill, and practically no tail.

As in the loons, the legs are placed far back, with the result that grebes are almost helpless on land. Hence, except for time spent incubating eggs on a floating nest, these birds spend all their non-flying time on water. The feet are provided with paddle-like extensions to the toes, which, together with the rearward position, make them efficient swimming organs.

Food on salt water is mostly small fishes captured in underwater pursuit. On fresh water aquatic insects and other animal forms are probably also taken.

Grebes nest on fresh water, but at other seasons of the year many of them resort to salt water. At times during the period of moult on the sea, grebes are flightless and entirely dependent on diving and swimming for escape. Diving is accomplished by a quick forward flip; sometimes the body can be slowly submerged until only the neck and head are visible.

Five species are present in British Columbia, as follows:—

Western Grebe.—Size large (28 inches in total length) with a long, slender neck. Black on top of head, back of neck, and on back; remainder silvery white. In breeding plumage a slight crest is present over each ear.

Red-necked Grebe.—Size medium (19 inches in total length), neck shorter than in the western grebe.   In winter, dark grey on top of head, white on cheek, grey on the neck and back, white on the underparts.   In summer, black on top of head and back of neck, chestnut red on the front and sides of the neck.

Horned Grebe.—Size small (13 inches in total length). Bill slender and sharp. In winter, dark grey on back of head and neck and on the back; remainder white. In summer, prominent yellow ear-tufts or " horns " behind the eyes and a black ruff on each side of the head; neck and upper breast chestnut brown.

Eared Grebe.—Almost indistinguishable in size and winter plumage from the horned grebe. In summer, golden feathers on the cheek and helmet-like crest on the crown; neck black.

Pied-bill Grebe.—Size small (13 inches in total length) but bill short and stubby. In winter, grey above and grey to white below. In summer, a black vertical bar through the light-coloured bill and a black patch on the throat.

Cormorants

Large, heavy-looking black-coloured diving birds with a long neck and a slender bill hooked at the tip. An unfeathered throat-pouch is usually present.

Cormorants capture small fishes by direct under-water pursuit. Swimming is accomplished entirely by leg action, yet so efficiently that agile fishes can be taken with ease. The birds can remain submerged for thirty to forty seconds and can reach a depth of 30 fathoms. After a number of dives, cormorants perch out of water and extend their wings as if to dry them. Actually this action helps restore the trapped air which has been expelled from the feathers by water pressure.

Cormorants nest in colonies on rock ledges overhanging the water, on rocky islets, and sometimes in trees. Nesting-sites are often conspicuously marked by droppings, which give a white-washed appearance to the rock.

There species of cormorants are found on the coast of British Columbia, as follows:—

Double-crested Cormorant.—Large in size (36 inches in total length); all black in colour but with a greenish sheen. Bare face and throat-pouch orange-yellow. Two filamentous dark plumes over each ear at beginning of nesting season.

Brandt Cormorant.—Large in size (35 inches in total length); all black in colour with a greenish or bluish tinge. Bare face and throat-pouch blue, bordered by a fawn-coloured patch. No crests

but sometimes with yellowish filaments on side of neck.

Pelagic Cormorant.—Smaller in size (25 inches in total length); black with purple and green sheen. Bare face and throat-pouch red. In the breeding season has a small double crest and a conspicuous white patch on the lower flank on each side.

52

Great Blue Heron

A large, long-legged wading bird with a slender neck and a long, sharp-pointed bill.

The head is white with a black mask over and behind the eye, ending in a plume. The neck and breast are brownish or greyish and merge into slate-blue of the body and wings. The shoulders are black.

Herons may be seen stalking for fish in the shallows or standing motionless until the quarry comes within striking distance. Sometimes they perch upon masses of kelp or upon floating logs. Food consists mostly of small fishes, but they also take snakes, frogs, mice, and insects such as dragonflies.

In flight the neck is folded to draw the head back to the shoulders and the legs are extended behind. The alarm cry is a deep harsh " ark, ark, ark," which startles one when produced almost underfoot or at night.

Herons nest in colonies called " heronries," composed of a number of bulky platforms built in one or more trees.

53

Black Brant

A small dark-coloured goose with a white belly and rump.

In more detail, the head, neck, breast, and main feathers of wings and tail are black, while the back and upper abdomen are brownish-black. White extends over the belly and on the underparts of the tail, giving a distinctive appearance to the bird both on the water and in flight. A whitish neck band is also present.

"In flight, brant travel in flocks of varying size, and usually at low levels. The flock appears as an undulating line in the distance bunching up at first at one side, then on the other. The line ripples and waves as individual birds gain or lose altitude, and all the while the whole line seems to climb and descend as the flock moves along. The wings appear to be set well back in the body, and the leading edge slopes back sharply, a feature by which brant may be identified at a great distance." (Guiguet, 1958.)

Flocks of black brant and pelagic cormorants appear very similar in flight. However, the backward-sloping wings and a slower wing beat serve to distinguish the former.

The call of the brant is a low throaty " karr-onk, krr-onk," with no great carrying power but distinctive in character.

While most black brant winter south of British Columbia, a few remain around the Queen Charlotte Islands and a small population is usually found in the Boundary Bay area from October to late spring. More begin to appear on northward migration along the coast of British Columbia in January and February, the large flocks coming in March, April, and May, particularly along the east coast of Vancouver Island. By June most have moved north to the western Arctic, where they nest.

Brant depend mostly upon eel-grass for food, supplemented with sea-lettuce and other seaweeds.

Mallard

Our best-known duck, not to be confused with any other.

The male mallard is particularly distinctive with its iridescent green or blue head, yellow bill, and black and white tail with up-curled feathers. The purple wing patch is also conspicuous both at rest and in flight.

The female is more or less drab brown in colour but also has a bright wing-patch. She is the one that utters the characteristic " quack, quack," a sound which some persons associate erroneously with all ducks.

Mallards may nest almost anywhere in British Columbia, with the result that breeding birds and young may be seen on lakes and ponds throughout the Province and occasionally along the seashore.

Mallards eat a great variety of food items, which partially accounts for their success in maintaining numbers in spite of increased hunting pressure and increased effects of civilization. Many kinds of aquatic plants, including roots and seeds, are utilized, plus acorns, apples, peas, corn, and other agricultural crops.

Widgeon or Baldpate

A medium-sized dabbling duck with a white forehead and crown in the male.

The male widgeon is further distinguished by a speckled head, a white breast and abdomen, pinkish-brown sides, and black hind parts. The female is greyish-brown with white underparts. In flight both sexes show a conspicuously coloured wing-patch.

The call of the male is a soft whistle, " whee-whee-whew," with the accent on the last syllable.

The widgeon nests in the interior of the Province but winters along the coast. It is commonly seen on salt water during the fall, winter, and early spring months. It feeds mostly upon various sea-weeds, eel-grass, and other vegetation.

Shoveller

A heavy-set dabbling duck with a spoon-shaped bill.

The male shoveller or spoon-bill is a gaily marked bird with a bright-green head, white breast, reddish abdomen and sides, and black hind parts. The enlarged bill is particularly distinctive and serves to identify the bird from all others.

The female also has an enlarged bill, but otherwise differs from the male in being mostly light brown in colour.

The shoveller is commonly seen in the coastal area during the winter months. It frequents shallow water, where it feeds upon vegetation, seeds, and small animal-life strained from the water by the sieve-equipped bill. Sewer outfalls are particularly attractive to this bird, a fact which does not endear the species to the hunter.

Scaups or Blue-bills

Medium-sized diving ducks with black heads and breasts and blue bills in the males.

The males also have a light, vermiculated back and white underparts; the ends of the wings and the tail are dark. Females are largely brown with white underparts.

There are two species of scaups, called the " greater " and the " lesser." The greater scaup is the larger in size, and in the male the white area on the wing feathers extends almost the entire length of the wing (leading bird in the illustration). In the lesser scaup the white area is much more restricted in size (male in background).

The female greater scaup (uppermost bird) differs from her counterpart in having more white around the bill and on the wing.

The greater scaup is common along the British Columbia coast from October through March, and sometimes associated with them are a few lesser scaups. Occasionally the latter are also found on lakes during the winter season.

Scaups feed upon a variety of animal and plant forms and are usually considered to be unpalatable while living along the coast.

Golden-eye Ducks

Medium-sized diving ducks, the males with a black head marked with a conspicuous white cheek-patch.

Male golden-eyes are also white on the neck, breast, and underparts and have some white wing feathers. The back and tail are black; the eye is golden. In the female the head is brown, the neck and underparts are white, the rest of the body is greyish.

Two kinds of golden-eye ducks are present in British Columbia—the Barrow and the American. The male of the former is recognized by the cheek-patch being crescent-shaped, while in the American it is circular. The females of the two species can be distinguished only with difficulty. (*See* references for further details.)

Both golden-eyes may be seen on salt water during the winter months. In late February or early March they begin to leave for breeding-grounds away from the coast.

Old Squaw Duck

A medium-sized diving duck, largely white and with long tail feathers in the male.

The male old squaw is distinctive in winter with its white head, neck, shoulders, and underparts. The back and the breast are black; the cheek-patch and wings are dark brown. The central tail feathers are long and pointed.

The female is light brown on the back and almost white below. The head is white on the sides, brown on the top, and with a brown patch below and behind the eye. The long tail feathers are lacking.

The call of the old squaw is as distinctive as its appearance, and once heard is likely to be remembered. It has a clarion quality to it, quite unlike that of any other bird, and may be represented by the syllables " a-leedle-a."

As the breeding season approaches, the male becomes black on the head, neck, shoulders, and breast, and the female also becomes darker. However, most birds leave the coast before May to nest in the subarctic tundra, and, as a result, birds in full breeding plumage are seldom seen on salt water.

Old squaws dive for shell-fish and other bottom-loving animals.

-F.L. Beebe

Harlequin Duck

A colourful medium-sized diving duck locally common along rocky shores.

Next to the wood duck the male harlequin is our most colourful waterfowl, distinguished chiefly by a complicated pattern of white on a blue and chestnut-brown background.

The female is drab in comparison, being dull greyish-brown above and whitish below. Indistinct white patches are present on the face.

Harlequins leave the sea-coast in April or May to nest on fresh-water streams. The male returns to salt water about mid-June and proceeds to moult into drab plumage resembling that of the female. For the remainder of the summer the drakes are flightless and are most commonly seen around kelp-beds close to rocky shore-lines. When pursued they dive or flop clumsily along the surface.

Harlequins feed almost entirely upon shell-fish and other marine animals while in salt water.

The Scoters

Large, heavy-bodied dark-coloured ducks with thick-set ornate bills (males).

Three species are found along the British Columbia coast, as follows:—

White-winged Scoter.—The male is black and the female is sooty brown, except for a broad white patch on each wing and small white markings on the face. In the male the face mark is a comma-shaped patch behind the eye. In the female one or two indistinct light patches may be behind the eye or they may be completely lacking.

American Scoter.—Male all black except for a bright-yellow bulb at the base of the bill.   Female dark brown except the side of the head and throat, which is lighter in colour and flecked with brown.

Surf Scoter.—Male all black but with a conspicuous white patch on the forehead and on the back of the head. The bill is much swollen and appears to merge with the head. The upper side is orange and yellow; the base is white, with a prominent black spot. Female dull brownish to slate on the back and sides. The head is darker, with two lighter patches on each cheek and one on the back of the head. The bill is swollen but not brightly coloured.

All three species leave the coast in the spring to nest, the white-winged scoter to lakes in the interior of the Province, the American to the coast of Alaska, and the surf scoter to the mouth of the Mackenzie River. They all appear again along our sea-coast in September and October.

Scoters feed upon mussels, small clams, crabs, and other shellfish, which they procure by diving.

F.L. Beebe

Mergansers

Fish-eating waterfowl with a narrow, toothed bill and with a crest on the head (except in the male American merganser).

Three species occur in British Columbia—American merganser, red-breasted merganser, and hooded merganser. *See* Guiguet (1958) or other references for distinguishing characteristics.

Bald Eagle

A large soaring bird with a white head and tail in the adult.

The white of the head extends down the neck to the shoulders; the body and wings are dark brown or almost black. Young birds are over-all dark brown for the first two years of life.

Along the coast the bald eagle is largely a scavenger, feeding upon dead fish and other animals cast up on the beach, but it will also capture living fish and birds as the opportunity arises.

Eagles are found throughout the length of the coast and are resident all year round.

Bald eagles are not bald! The name comes from piebald meaning " of different colours, especially white and black."

The cry of the bald eagle is a series of weakly whistled high-pitched notes, " hee-hee-hee-hee-hee," a most disappointing sound for a bird so large and impressive as an eagle.

American Coot

A medium-sized dark-coloured bird with a white bill.

Colour slate-grey, darkening to black on the neck and head. Base of white bill broadens to form a shield on the forehead, above which is a reddish-brown spot. Legs green with lobed toes.

Coots nest in marshy lakes both near the coast and in the interior of the Province. In the fall they gather in great numbers on both fresh and salt water. Their call-note is a metallic " cluck."

Shorebirds

A large number of waders may be grouped under this general heading. These are mostly smaller than a robin in size, but a few are larger than a pigeon. All have relatively long legs with no webs or very small webs between the toes; in some the bill is extraordinarily long. Many of them frequent the intertidal zone, where they probe the mud or sand for small worms, crustaceans, and other organisms.

Most species nest in the north or away from the coast; consequently, they are seen along the shore only on migration. This is usually April and May, when the birds are moving northward, and again in late July and August, when the first south-bound migrants appear. At these times great flocks of waders may occur in certain areas, often made up of several species mixed together.

As the smaller shorebirds are often difficult to identify even by experts, no attempt is made in this publication to identify the various species. Illustrations and brief accounts of a few of the more easily recognized species are offered here, and the reader is referred to the list of references for further details.

Black Oyster Catcher.—A large, heavy-set black shorebird with a long flattened red bill and pale-coloured legs.

The plumage is dull black in colour, the eye is bright yellow rimmed with red, and the feet are unwebbed.

Oyster catchers are present along the entire coastline, particularly on the rocky exposed sections. They feed on shell-fish, which they open by means of the flattened bill, plus other animal forms found between tide-levels.

The cry is a piercing, sharply repeated whistled note, " eep eep eep eep eep," which may be heard for a considerable distance over the water.

They are migratory to some extent, but some birds usually remain the winter in most areas.

Surf Bird.—A chunky grey and white shorebird a little larger than a robin. In flight, black and white markings on the wings and tail are conspicuous. In summer plumage (bird in foreground), the breast and flanks show V-shaped black marks.

Black Turnstone.—A shorebird with dark head, back, and breast. In flight, white wing-bars, white rump, and white belly are conspicuous.

(The uncommon ruddy turnstone has a white head marked with black, a glossy black chest, red legs, and rufous-coloured feathers on the back.)

Red-backed Sandpiper. — In winter, grey and white plumage with dark wing-tips. In summer, the back is red and the belly has a black patch.

Baird Sandpiper.—Feathers of the back and sides have white margins; underparts are silver-grey. The body is smaller and the bill is shorter than that of the red-backed sandpiper.

Northern Phalarope.—In fall and winter, largely white with a striped grey and black back, a black cap, and a dark bar through the eye.

In spring and summer, dark grey on the head, face, and back and extending partially across the breast. The throat-patch is white and the sides of the neck are brick red.

Northern phalaropes are most often seen in late summer and early fall while on their southward migration, when they may occur in great numbers well out to sea and also in protected waters about the southern end of Vancouver Island. Unlike the other shore-birds, phalaropes take to the water and consequently are most often observed swimming. They ride high on the surface and often swim in a whirligig pattern, which is most characteristic.

Another well-known peculiarity of phalaropes is that the female is brighter coloured than the male and does the courting. The male, in turn, incubates the eggs and rears the young.

Red Phalarope.—A little larger in size and with a stouter bill. Plumage pattern as shown in the illustration.

The red phalarope is only occasionally seen in coastal waters.

Glaucous-winged Gull

A typical gull, large in size and with wings pale grey on the upper surface. This is the common " sea-gull " resident along the coast the year round.

The adult glaucous-winged gull is easily identified by its large size (length to 27 inches) and light-grey wings with *no* black tip. The bill is yellow with a bright red spot on the lower mandible, and the feet are flesh-coloured. The head, tail, and underparts are pure white.

Birds in their first year are more or less greyish-brown in colour all over, and those in their second year are paler. Adult plumage is not attained until the third year.

Glaucous-winged gulls nest on rocky islets along many parts of our coast. Two to four large heavily blotched olive or green to brown-coloured eggs are laid in late May or early June, and downy young are usually present in July.

Glaucous-winged gulls eat a wide variety of food, including small fish, which they catch near the surface, stranded starfishes, crabs, dead fish, and other carrion and garbage in general. Hard-shelled creatures such as sea-urchins and molluscs are broken by dropping them on rock or nearby roadway. On occasion this gull will also attack, kill, and devour the young of ducks and other water-birds.

Each year numbers of gulls are banded by persons interested in learning details of life-history and movements. Any gull found with a numbered metal band on the leg should be reported to the Fish and Wildlife Service, Washington, D.C., as directed on the band, or to the Provincial Museum, Victoria, B.C.

Herring Gull

A large gull very similar in appearance to the glaucous-winged gull, differing mainly in having black wing-tips.

Herring gulls nest on lakes in the interior of the Province and hence are absent or nearly so on the coast during the summer. Some gulls remain on lakes in the southern portion of the Province throughout the year, but the majority of them move out to salt water after the breeding season and hence are abundant during fall and winter.

Like the glaucous-winged gull, the herring gull feeds on whatever opportunity presents, even following the plough for grubs and other insects.

F.L.Beebe

Bonaparte Gull

A small, slender gull with a conspicuous black head and bluish-grey on the upper surface of the body and wings. The tail and underparts are white; the bill is black and the feet light-coloured.

Since the Bonaparte gull nests in the central and northern interior of the Province, it is absent from the coast during the breeding season. Adults and young begin to appear on salt water in early July and August. At this time most adults have the distinctive black head, a plumage pattern which they lose during the fall moult. By winter all are white-headed, the young birds being distinguished from adults by the presence of a black border to the tail. Most take on adult breeding plumage, marked particularly by the black head, by March, April, and May, when the spring migration begins.

Bonaparte gulls feed mostly on small herring and sandlance, which they catch by plunging a short distance beneath the surface. A flock of excited birds usually marks the position of a school of fish forced to the surface by feeding salmon, thus providing a useful indication for the sports fisherman.

Other Gulls

About twenty species of gulls and their relatives occur in British Columbia, and many of them are difficult to identify by sight because they undergo several plumage changes. Details and helpful hints on identification will be found in the publications listed under references.

Murre

A large black and white diving bird with a moderately long bill and a short tail.

The head and neck are dark brown; the back and wings are black. As in a number of water-birds, the legs are placed far back on the body, causing the murre to assume an upright penguin-like stance when on land.

In summer the white of the underparts is sharply marked off from the dark brown at the base of the neck.

In winter the white of the underparts extends up the front of the neck and over the side of the head. The top of the head and neck are black, and a black line extends back from the eye.

Murres are fish-eating birds that nest in large colonies on rocky ledges usually facing the open sea. They are usually absent from inside waters during the breeding season but begin to appear in the early fall and stay the winter.

For some reason, murres seem most susceptible to the effects of oil, which is occasionaly present on inshore waters. The feathers of oiled birds lose their ability to repel water, with the result that the birds become chilled and are forced out of the water in order to keep warm. On shore the birds slowly die of the combined effects of exposure and starvation. Often while awaiting their end, murres are mistaken for penguins because of their upright stance and black-and white appearance.

Pigeon Guillemot

A small black (summer) diving bird with a conspicuous white wing-patch and bright red legs and feet. The bill and underparts are black, and the white wing-patch is divided by a black bar.

In winter, guillemots are more white than black, but the wings retain the same colour pattern.

Guillemots may be seen at all seasons along the entire coast of British Columbia. In summer they nest under boulders or rock slabs above high tide, in rock crevices on a cliff face, or in burrows. They feed mostly on small fishes, especially pricklebacks, which they capture by diving in kelp-beds.

The cry is a thin whistle.

Marbled Murrelet

A small dumpy diving bird with a round head, short bill, and short tail.

In summer, brown in over-all colour, reddish on the back, mottled on the underparts. In winter, both adults and young blackish above, darker on the crown, and white below to chin.

The marbled murrelet is found along the entire coast and is most abundant in the Queen Charlotte Islands. Despite its large numbers, nesting colonies remain undiscovered.

Murrelets are readily recognized by the fact they ride high on the water and carry the bill and tail at a jaunty angle. They dive with a quick forward flip, exposing the white bottom briefly.

Food consists of small fishes and crustaceans.

Ancient Murrelet

Similar in general appearance to the marbled murrelet. In summer, slaty-blue above, white below. Head, hind neck, cheek, and throat black. In winter, much the same plumage. Less white on the head than in the marbled murrelet.

The ancient murrelet nests in the Queen Charlotte Islands and other islands to the north, and consequently is not ordinarily seen along the southern coast in summer. For the winter months it migrates southward as far as California.

Belted Kingfisher

A noisy blue and white bird with a prominent crest and a strong, sharp bill.

The head, back, wings, and tail are a dark slaty blue, as is the "belt" across the chest. The throat, lower neck, and the belly are white.

The kingfisher patrols the shallow water near shore in a characteristic undulating flight, pausing to hover over a likely spot and finally to plunge beneath the surface with a splash. Considerable time is also spent perching on overhanging branches or any similar commanding position. These habits plus its distinctive appearance and rattling cry make it an easy bird to identify.

REFERENCES

Guiguet, C. J. 1955. The Birds of British Columbia: (3) The Shorebirds. B.C. Prov. Museum Handbook No. 8, pp. 1–54.
——— 1957. The Birds of British Columbia: (5) Gulls, Terns, Jaegers, and Skua. B.C. Prov. Museum Handbook No. 13, pp. 1–42.
——— 1958. The Birds of British Columbia: (6) Waterfowl. B.C. Prov. Museum Handbook No. 15, pp. 1–84.
Peterson, Roger Tory. 1961. A Field Guide to Western Birds. Houghton Mifflin Co.
Taverner, P. A. 1934. Birds of Canada. National Museum of Canada, Bull. No. 72.

FISHES

Most fishes are relatively easy to classify as to group to which they belong, whether salmon, rockfish, or shark for example, but the identification as to species is often much more difficult. Many an argument among anglers as to the identity of the catch can only be settled by calling in the help of some expert or authority in ichthyology. The following notes may help in the identification of some of the commoner species, but when difficulty is encountered a more detailed text should be consulted or the fish in question should be taken to someone with experience and expert knowledge.

In checking descriptions you may need to know the following terms:—

Rays (in fin)—flexible rods which support the fin.

Spines (in fin)—stiff, bony rods supporting the fin.

Dorsal fin—the fin in the centre of the back.

Anal fin—the single fin beneath the tail.

Ventral or pelvic fins—the pair of fins under the belly, corresponding to hind limbs on a land animal.

Pectoral fins—the pair of side fins, corresponding to fore-limbs in land animals.

Gill rakers—bony tooth-like structures on each gill arch, designed for straining out food items.

Pyloric cæca—finger-like processes attached to the intestine immediately behind the stomach.

Peduncle—the narrowest part of the fish's body just before the tail fin.

Lateral line—the row of perforated scales which usually extends along each side of a fish from a point behind the gill cover to the base of the tail. It is sensitive to vibrations or pressure changes in the water.

Basking Shark   *Cetorhinus maximus* **(Gunner)**

A very large shark with a triangular dorsal fin and prominent tail fin, both of which may project above the water as the fish lies or swims at the surface.

Five long gill slits on each side, extending almost to the mid-line on the ventral surface. A prominent keel on each side of the base of the tail.

Colour bluish-grey to brownish-grey, paler on the undersurface.

Size up to 45 feet in total length. Those in British Columbia usually range between 20 and 30 feet.

The basking shark is the largest fish in British Columbia and the second largest in the world, being exceeded only by the whale shark in size. It occurs regularly in the Barkley Sound area on the west coast of Vancouver Island and occasionally in Saanich Arm and elsewhere along the east coast of Vancouver Island, as well as the mainland coast.

While resting near the surface, a habit which gives it its common name, this shark may be approached quite readily. However, it is unwise to do so in a small boat. While the fish is harmless as far as feeding habits are concerned, it may accidentally swamp a boat or damage it by a blow from the tail in its efforts to sound quickly.

The basking shark feeds on small organisms, which it strains from the water as it swims. The gill rakers are especially developed to form an effective sieve for this purpose.

As in all sharks, the skeleton is of cartilage. Occasionally a partial skeleton is found on the beach, when it may give rise to a report of a "sea-serpent" because of its great length and general serpentine appearance.

Dogfish   *Squalus suckleyi* **(Girard)**

A small shark with a spine in each of two dorsal fins.

Body cigar-shaped and covered with small spiny scales. A prominent spiracle (breathing pore) behind the eye. Five gill slits on each side behind the head. The upper part of the tail fin is longer than the lower, as is the case in all sharks.

Colour grey or dark brown on the back and whitish on the undersurface. Young dogfish have light spots on the back.

Size up to 5 feet 3 inches in length, but the average is about 30 inches.

Anglers consider dogfish a pest because they often take the lure, occupying the time and trying the patience of the fisherman when he would rather catch more desirable fish.

Dogfish usually travel in schools. They prey on small fishes, such as herring, anchovy, and smelts, and also on crabs and squids. They are destructive to certain fishing-gear and to netted fish, with the result that the Federal Government has paid a bounty or subsidy on them from time to time.

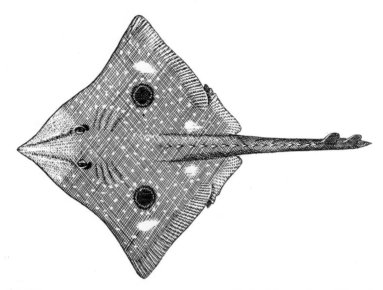

Big Skate *Raja binoculata* **Girard**

A large flattened fish with a long slender tail.

Snout pointed; a prominent spiracle (breathing pore) behind the eye. Five gill slits on the ventral surface. A series of large spines along the mid-line of the back and tail.

Colour brownish, grey, or nearly black on the upper surface with a prominent black " eye-spot " on each side, each within a dark ring. (The light ring in each eye-spot is reddish in young fish.) Many white spots scattered over the body. Undersurface almost dead white.

Length up to 8 feet. Large individuals more than 9 feet from tip to tip across the back have been reported.

The big skate is the largest species found in British Columbia. It lives along the coast at depths varying from shallow to moderate. Occasionally individuals are seen in water only a few feet deep, especially over mud flats on an incoming tide.

Food consists mostly of crustaceans and fishes; two sculpins, each about a foot long, were found in one stomach.

As in all skates, water is drawn into the breathing chamber through the spiracles on top of the head and is expelled through the gill slits on the underside.

Two to seven eggs are laid at any season in a parchment-like case ranging in length up to 12 inches; they may require a year to hatch. The egg case is sometimes called a " mermaid's purse " when found cast up on the beach.

In addition to the big skate, the longnose skate, the starry skate, the black skate, and the deepsea skate occur in British Columbia.

Coho Salmon   *Oncorhynchus kisutch* (Walbaum)

A typical salmon usually with black spots on the back and upper half of the tail fin.

Head conical in shape, but as the fish nears spawing-time the snout becomes hooked, particularly in the male. Gill rakers on the first arch from 19 to 25. Rays in the anal fin from 13 to 16. Scales in the first row above the lateral line from 120 to 145. Pyloric cæca from 45 to 83.

Colour usually bluish-green on the back, shading to silver and then white on the belly. Usually many irregular black spots on the back and on the upper half of the tail fin only. As the fish approaches spawning-time, it becomes much darker, particularly on the head, and the sides become reddish.

Average length about 28 to 30 inches and weight 6 to 12 pounds. (World's record on sport tackle, 36 inches in length and 31½ pounds in weight by Mrs. Lee Halberg, of Victoria, in 1947.)

There is no single " sure fire " method of identifying a coho; cohoes vary so greatly in size and outward appearance, depending upon age and proximity to spawning-time, that some are most difficult to recognize.

If you have a " sticker," first count the rays in the anal fin to make sure it is a salmon. If there are only 12, it may be a steelhead; if more than 12, it is definitely a Pacific salmon. Next check the presence of black spots on the tail fin. Spots on the upper half only indicate a coho; spots on the entire fin are characteristic of a chinook salmon.

However, some cohoes have no spots on the tail, in which case count the number of scales in the row above the lateral line (120 to 145 for coho; 140 to 153 for spring or chinook). If the count falls in the overlap (140 to 145) or if there is still doubt, count the pyloric cæca. This is not only a messy job, since it entails opening the body cavity to expose the stomach and intestine, but it is also difficult to do because these flabby finger-like organs are so closely bunched that accurate counting is almost impossible. However, it is usually fairly easy to determine whether or not the number of cæca falls within the coho count of 45 to 83 or exceeds 140, which is the minimum number in a chinook salmon.

If still there remains some question of identity, then take the whole fish to any one of the following institutions: Provincial Museum, Victoria; Biological Station, Nanaimo; Institute of Fisheries, University of British Columbia, Vancouver; Provincial Fish and Game Branch, Victoria; Vancouver Public Aquarium, Vancouver; International Pacific Salmon Commission, New Westminster.

Cohoes usually spawn in tributaries of coastal streams in November and December, and the fry begin to appear in April. The majority of them migrate to sea in the spring of their second year of life, and during the ensuing year they make up a large proportion of those fish called " grilse " by sport fishermen. (The term " grilse " actually refers to the young of all species of salmon and trout while in salt water.) However, for fishery regulation purposes a grilse is a " salmon of 3 pounds in weight or less undressed."

During the winter and spring of their third year, cohoes are often called " bluebacks," particularly within the fishing industry. At this time they range about 3 to 5 pounds in weight. In this their final summer they feed heavily and grow rapidly, often doubling their weight in a few months. By fall, at the end of their third year, they mature, enter streams to spawn, and die.

Cohoes are primarily fish-eaters, feeding mainly on sandlance and herring; squids, euphausids (a kind of shrimp), and other invertebrates are also taken.

Chinook Salmon   *Oncorynchus tshawytscha* (**Walbaum**)

A typical salmon, usually with black spots on the back and on *both* upper and lower portions of the tail fin.

Gill rakers on the first arch from 18 to 30. Rays in the anal fin from 13 to 19. Scales in the first row above the lateral line from 140 to 153. Pyloric cæca from 140 to 185.

Colour usually greenish-blue to black on the back, shading to silver and then white on the belly. Many irregular black spots on back, dorsal fin, and both upper and lower portions of the tail fin.

Average length about 36 inches and weight 10 to 50 pounds. (A record fish weighing 126 pounds, 53 inches long, was taken at Petersburg, Alaska, in 1948.)

The chinook salmon is also known as spring, quinnat, and king salmon. Those 30 or more pounds in weight are often called " tyee " by sports fishermen.

Most chinook salmon become mature in their third to seventh year. Males which mature in their second or third year, while still relatively small in size, are commonly called " jacks."

Pink Salmon; Humpback

Oncorhynchus gorbuscha (Walbaum)

A typical salmon with fine scales and oval black blotches on back and on tail fin.

Gill rakers on the first arch from 24 to 35. Rays in the anal fin from 13 to 17. Scales in the first row above the lateral line from 170 to 229 (therefore, scales are much smaller than in other species of salmon).

Colour usually metallic blue on the back, silvery on the sides, and white on the belly. Oval-shaped black blotches are usually present on the back and on the tail fin. Males approaching maturity become red on the sides, blotched with brown, and the back develops a pronounced hump (hence the common name " humpback ").

Length up to 30 inches and weight from 3 to 10 pounds.

Ordinarily pink salmon do not take a lure, but occasionally they do, at which time large numbers may be taken by sport fishermen.

Pink salmon live only two years. They begin life as fry which emerge from the gravel in the spring and migrate almost at once down-stream to the sea. Major growth takes place in the second season; by fall the adults enter streams to spawn and die. Spawning fish usually remain near tidal water, but occasionally some travel long distances, for example, to the upper reaches of the Skeena River.

Herring   *Clupea pallasii* **Valenciennes**

A small silvery fish, usually travelling in large schools.

Mouth capable of being extended to form a tube; tail moderately forked. Scales large and easily shed.

Colour bluish-green or blue on the back and iridescent silver on the sides and belly. Average length from 10 to 12 inches but occasionally up to 18 inches.

Spawning takes place in late winter or early spring, when the eggs are laid, mostly in the intertidal zone. Usually the eggs are fastened to seaweeds, rocks, piles, and other supports, but some-times they are so abundant they become piled up by wave action in windrows along the beach, where they attract great numbers of birds, crabs, and other animals.

Young herring are commonly seen schooling in shallow water. They may be distinguished by their peculiar habit of " flashing "; at intervals individuals in the school turn momentarily on their side, producing a silvery flash that catches the eye.

Larger herring frequent deeper water, where bait-catchers locate them by using a herring jig or by using an echo sounder.

Herring are probably the most widely used source of protein in coastal waters. They are eaten by fishes of many kind and sizes, by squids, porpoises, seals, sea-lions, whales, birds, and man. In commercial value they are second only to salmon.

Shiner Seaperch   *Cymatogaster aggregata* **Gibbons**

A small silvery perch-like fish frequenting wharves.

Head short, mouth small with protrusible lips. Dorsal fin long with 8 to 11 spines followed by 18 to 23 rays. Tail fin strongly forked. Scales large.

Colour silvery with a dark back and a series of longitudinal dark stripes on the side. Three vertical yellow bars on each flank. Males are very dark in winter and early spring.

Size up to 6 inches in length, rarely to 8 inches.

The shiner seapearch is somewhat similar to the fresh-water perch in appearance. It is commonly found in schools around piles and beneath floating wharves, where it searches among the barnacles and mussels for small animals as food.

As is the case with all seaperches, young are born alive. Mating takes place in spring and early summer and birth occurs ten to twelve months later. From eight to thirty-six young are produced at a time.

Several other members of this family are found in British Columbia, including the common striped seaperch and the pile seaperch. All are protected by a closed season during the months of June, July, and August in each year.

Lingcod   *Ophiodon elongatus* **Girard**

An elongated fish with a big head and a big mouth.

Head long and conical, lower jaw projecting; teeth large and rather prominent. A fleshy, plume-like structure over each eye. Dorsal fin long with 24 to 27 spines in the first portion, separated from the second by a shallow notch.

Colour may be black, brown, blue, or green on the back and greenish-grey or cream on the belly. The back, sides, dorsal and tail fins are frequently mottled. Males often have large dark greenish-brown areas on the back and sides outlined with tracings of pale blue or orange. Females are similarly marked but lighter and with orange tracings instead of blue.

Length up to 5 feet and weight to greater than 60 pounds.

Lingcod live near the bottom down to a least 60 fathoms and usually among kelp-beds and reefs, especially near strong tidal movements. They may be caught on either artificial or baited jigs or by trolling with a spoon or plug. Occasionally one will seize a rockfish that is being pulled up by an angler and both fish may be taken.

Lingcod spawn in the winter months and the male stands guard over the egg-mass. At this time he is particularly belligerent and may attack a skin diver who ventures too close.

Rockfishes   *Sebastodes* spp.

Medium-sized spiny-rayed fishes with a large head and mouth.

These are the fishes commonly called " rock cod " or in some cases " black bass." Twenty-five or more species of rockfishes are found in British Columbia. In each the head is large and usually provided with bony ridges and spines. The scales on the body are large and rough. The dorsal fin has 13 to 15 spines and 9 to 16 rays; both the anal fin and pelvic fins are also equipped with spines.

Many kinds are found along rocky shores in quite shallow water, but some go to considerable depths, 822 fathoms for example. In-shore species are largely brown in colour, while those in deep water, such as the snapper, tend to be red.

In all rockfishes the young are born alive and are produced in the summer months. At birth they are almost transparent, about one-half inch in length and in great numbers.

REFERENCES

Carl, G. Clifford; Clemens, W. A.; and Lindsay, C. C. 1959. The Fresh-water Fishes of British Columbia. B.C. Prov. Museum Handbook No. 5, pp. 1–192.

Clemens, W. A., and Wilby, G. V. 1961. Fishes of the Pacific Coast of Canada. Bull. 68 (2nd ed.), pp. 1–443.

Norman, J. R., and Fraser, F. C. 1949. Field Book of Giant Fishes. G. P. Putnam's Sons, New York.

Commercial Fisheries Branch. 1959. The Commercial Fisheries of British Columbia. Department of Recreation and Conservation, pp. 1–36.

JELLYFISHES

Many kinds of jellyfishes occur in the coastal waters of British Columbia, and a few of them are large enough or numerous enough to attract wide attention. All are jelly-like in structure, with the body parts laid out like an umbrella or mushroom in general plan. All have tentacles provided with stinging cells used in capturing small animals for food, and some are capable of stinging humans.

Sea Jellyfish   *Aquorea aquorea* (**Forsakali**)

A flattened disk-shaped jellyfish with numerous canals radiating from a central stomach.

Edge of disk with many tentacles, each with a swollen base and each capable of great extension. Lobes around mouth very small.

The sea jellyfish is colourless and translucent; at night it glows with a greenish luminescence.

Size up to 3 inches or more in diameter.

The sea jellyfish is possibly the most numerous species in British Columbia. It occurs in great numbers all along the coast and is often conspicuous around floats or wharves, drifting in the current near the surface.

Batteries of stinging cells on the tentacles enable this jellyfish to capture and kill small fishes and other active animals for food.

Moon Jellyfish   *Aurelia labiata* **Chamisso and Eysenhardt**

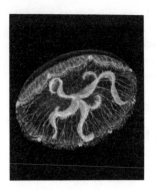

A flattened disk-shaped jellyfish with four prominent U-shaped structures arranged like a cross.

Four long narrow lobes or arms surround the mouth and hang down below the disk. The edge of the disk has 16 equally-spaced indentations and carries a fringe of small tentacles. Many branching canals radiate from the four-lobed stomach to join a circular canal just within the edge of the disk.

Moon jellyfish are colourless, except for the U-shaped reproductive organs, which are brown, yellow, or orange.

Size up to 10 inches in diameter; average diameter between 6 and 7 inches.

Moon jellyfish are remarkable because they are so locally abundant at times. They are not particularly noticeable in open water, but in certain bays and arms they may become trapped until they occur in great numbers so that one seems to be cruising through a sea of jellyfishes.

As in a number of jellyfish species, the life-history is complicated by a vegetative stage. Eggs are discharged into the water, where they are fertilized by sperms from another individual. The fertilized egg becomes a swimming organism which soon settles on some solid support, where it develops into a tubular individual with a central mouth surrounded by a series of tentacles. In time the tubular stalk becomes divided into a stack of saucer-shaped disks; the outer one, bearing the tentacles, separates from those below to swim away as a tiny jellyfish, and the rest follow as they in turn acquire a mouth and tentacles. Each of these is either male or female, which in time attain adult size and begin to reproduce sexually.

Sea Blubber

Cyanea capillata **Eschscholz**

F.L.B.

A large jellyfish with a flat, brightly coloured disk and long tentacles.

The margin of the disk is deeply notched to form 8 lobes, each of which is further indented by a shallow cleft. Four long, greatly ruffled lobes surround the mouth, and these, together with several hundred long tentacles, trail beneath the disk.

The colour is variable, ranging from brownish to bright yellow, orange, or pink.

Size up to 20 inches in diameter. (Individuals up to 7 feet in diameter are said to occur in the Atlantic Ocean.)

The large size and bright colour usually bring this jellyfish to the attention of the most casual observer. It may be found anywhere along the coastline drifting with the tide through the innumerable channels of inshore waters, far out to sea, or cast up on the beach.

The stinging cells of sea blubber are sufficiently potent to irritate human skin in contact with them and to cause severe discomfort. The poison produced contains several toxins, some of which cause paralysis of certain nerve endings, sleepiness, itching of the skin, digestive disturbances, and difficulties in breathing. The effects usually subside after three hours; some relief may be gained by rubbing with glycerine, baking-soda, or liniment.

These jellyfish are a menace, particularly to fishermen and to bathers who may come in to direct contact with them. They are the only marine animal which one should not touch with bare hands.

REFERENCES

Carter, Neal M.   1943.   The Stinging Action of Jellyfishes.   Fish. Res. Bd., Canada, Progress Report, Pacific, No. 55, pp. 7–9.

Guberlet, Muriel Lewin.   1936.   Animals of the Seashore.   Binfords & Mort, Portland, Ore.

Ricketts, Edward F., and Calvin, Jack.   1952.   Between Pacific Tides.   Stanford University Press.

Smith, Lynwood.   1962.   Common Seashore Life of the Pacific Northwest.   Naturegraph Company, Healdsburg, Calif.

STARFISHES AND RELATIVES

The starfishes, sea urchins, sand dollars, sea cucumbers, and other members of this large group all have a spiny or warty skin sometimes supported with limy plates, and the body plan is radial as in the jellyfishes and their kin. Most also have structures called " tube feet," which are organs used in locomotion. Each tube foot is a hollow structure ending in a sucker, and each capable of being greatly extended or contracted to push or pull the animal along the bottom.

Starfishes, with their striking shape and brilliant colour, are sometimes the most conspicuous feature of a beach at low tide. Many species occur along the British Columbia shoreline. Three of the most noticeable ones are illustrated here.

Purple or Ochre Starfish   *Pisaster ochraceus* (Brandt)

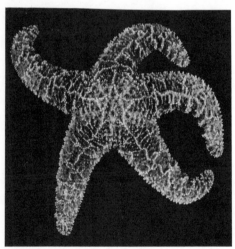

(Photo by A. R. Fontaine.)

A large star with broad arms and rough skin. The five arms taper from a thick-set disk, on the underside of which is a central mouth. The upper surface has many short spines arranged in a network.

The most common colour is purple, but yellow, orange, or brown individuals are also found.

Size up to 20 inches in diameter.

The purple star is the most abundant starfish to be seen at low tide along some beaches, and it is probably the most conspicuous because of its size and bright colour. It feeds on barnacles, mussels, and clams, opening the latter by direct pull on the shell produced by the tube feet. If the clam is too large to swallow, the walls of the stomach are everted to digest the victim outside the body of the starfish. When digestion is complete, the stomach is returned to its normal position and the starfish resumes its search for more food.

The power of regeneration in starfish is highly developed. If an arm is lost, a new one soon grows to take its place. Moreover, the dismembered arm is also capable of reproducing the lacking portions under certain conditions, so it is not unusual to see starfishes in various stages of replacing lost parts.

Mottled Star   *Evasterias troschelii* (Stimson)

A large narrow-armed starfish with a small central disk.

Numerous spines on the upper surface form an irregular network or scattered groups, and the colour pattern is mottled brown and green.

Size up to 24 inches in diameter.

The mottled star is sometimes common in quiet water at low-tide levels. A special kind of sea-worm is often found living in the

(Photo by A. R. Fontaine.)

groove on the underside of this starfish. The worm is not a parasite, but a " free boarder " known as a " commensal," which lives harmlessly with its host.

Sunflower Star

Pycnopodia helianthoides (Brandt)

A large star with many arms radiating from a broad disk.

Arms may number up to 24, depending upon the size and age of the starfish. Upper surface has thick, soft skin with numbers of short, scattered spines projecting through.

Colour usually soft pink, but it may be yellow, orange, or purplish.

Size large, sometimes greater than 2 feet in diameter.

(Photo by B.C. Govt. Travel Bureau.)

The sunflower star is one of the largest starfishes in the world; individuals up to 32 inches in diameter have been recorded. Despite its size and bulk, the sunflower star can move quite rapidly, gliding with ease in any direction over sand, mud, or rock. It is a voracious feeder, preying upon molluscs or any animal it can capture.

Green Sea Urchin

Strongylocentrotus drobachiensis (Müller)

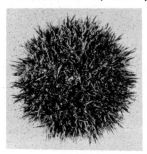

A spiny animal shaped like a flattened globe, up to 4 inches in diameter.

Spines are numerous and sharp, from one-half to three-quarters of an inch long. A mouth on the underside through which five teeth project.

Colour greenish, occasionally brown.

Great numbers of green sea urchins frequent crevices and caverns in rock and are exposed at extreme low tides.

Many also live in tide pools, where each (Photo by B.C. Govt. Travel Bureau.) animal may be found occupying a rock chamber, which gives it complete protection against surf action.

106

Two other similar species occur on rocky shores—the purple urchin (about the same size as the green urchin but purple in colour and with blunt spines) and the giant red urchin (up to 6½ inches in diameter and reddish-purple in colour).

Sand Dollar 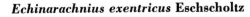*Echinarachnius exentricus* Eschscholtz

A very much flattened, nearly circular sea urchin with very short spines.

The flattened, circular shape and velvety black surface readily identify this urchin, and its empty shell is easily recognized because of its shape and the pattern of pores on its back like a five-petalled flower.

Size about 4 inches in diameter, but ranging up to 5½ inches in some localities.

(Photo by B.C. Govt. Travel Bureau.)

Living sand dollars may be found in sheltered bays almost buried in the sand near the low-tide level. Their presence is most often indicated by the empty white shells, sometimes called " sea biscuits," which may be found higher up on the beach.

Giant Sea Cucumber   *Stichopus californicus* (Stimpson)

A large cucumber-shaped soft-bodied animal with numerous warty projections.

Body cylindrical and slug-like with rows of tube feet on the underside and large conical protuberances on the upper side. A rosette of branched tentacles surrounds the mouth at one end.

Colour reddish-brown, sometimes mottled; tentacles tipped with yellow.

Size up to 18 inches in length.

These somewhat repulsive-looking members of the starfish group are most often seen on rocky shores below the low-tide level. Despite their appearance they are edible; the bands of muscle obtained by stripping off the tough outer skin make " good eating." In fact, related forms in the tropics are regularly harvested and sold as " trepang " or " bêche-de-mer."

CRABS

The true crabs along with hermit crabs, shrimps, mud shrimps, barnacles, and their kin make up the group called "crustaceans." All have a shell covering the body and the various limbs, and the limbs and other appendages are jointed.

Crabs and their relatives increase in size by a series of moults. First a new, soft shell forms beneath the old one; then the old shell splits at the back, forming an exit through which the animal backs out. Once free of the old cover the animal expands its body to its new size. During the process it hides in a safe place a few days until the new shell has hardened.

Edible Crab   *Cancer magister* **Dana**

A large crab with 10 teeth along the leading edge of the shell, the outermost one on each side being the longest.

As in all true crabs, there are 4 pairs of walking-legs and one pair of pincers. The eyes are on short stalks, and each can be folded into a recess for protection.

Colour purplish-brown on the upper surface; legs and lower surface brownish-white. (The colour turns decidedly red during cooking.)

Size up to 9 inches across the widest part of the back.

The edible crab is found on a sandy bottom, particularly around beds of eel-grass. A good part of its time is spent partly buried in the sand with only the antennæ and eyes showing above the surface. Its food is largely cockles and other clams, which it opens by chipping away the edge of the mollusc shell with the powerful pincers.

The legal minimum size of edible crabs is 6½ inches across the greatest breadth of the shell. Fishery regulations or officials should be consulted concerning certain closed areas and seasons.

Red Rock Crab   *Cancer productus Randall*

A medium-sized crab with the front margin of the shell scalloped with broad rounded spines and with 5 equally spaced teeth between the eyes. It is dark red in colour with black tips to the pincers.

Size up to 7 inches across the widest part of the back.

Rock crabs are most often seen on gravelly and rocky bottoms or beneath stones: While they are not used commercially, they are quite edible and are therefore frequently captured for food.

Purple Shore Crab

Hemigrapsus nudus (Dana)

A small crab with a squarish shell and red spots on the claws.

The front corners of the shell (carapace) are deeply notched, forming a recess for the stalked eyes. Males carry a soft pad on the inner surface of each claw.

Colour usually purplish, but the colour varies through reddish brown and greenish-yellow, sometimes with a mottled design. Red spots are nearly always present on the claws. The underside is pale.

Size up to 1¾ inches across the widest part of the back.

The purple shore crab is one of the most common inhabitants of the rocky beach; almost every boulder and stone will be found to shelter its quota of crabs, mostly of this species. They are able to stay out of the water for a considerable period of time, and consequently are sometimes found well up the beach.

Another common species, the hairy shore crab, is almost as abundant. It resembles the purple shore crab in size and shape, but lacks the red spots on the claws and the legs are fringed with short hairs.

111

Hairy Hermit Crab   *Pagarus hirsutiusculus* (Dana)

A hairy-looking crab usually occupying a too-small snail shell.

As in most hermit crabs, the right claw is much larger than the left. Both claws are granular in surface appearance.

Colour of large claw light, with white bands; walking-legs dark grey with dark longitudinal stripes.

Size up to 2 inches in length.

While most hermit crabs carry around an empty snail shell into which they can retreat, the hairy hermit wears a shell much too small to cover the entire body, but which allows it to move quickly. It is therefore rather conspicuous in tide pools and shallow water along the shoreline, where it may occur in quite large numbers.

Granular Hermit Crab   *Pagurus granosimanus* (Stimpson)

A hermit crab with granular pincers, red antennæ (feelers), and olive-green walking-legs spotted with white or blue.

Size up to 2 inches in length.

The granular hermit may often be seen in numbers, scurrying around in tide pools or in shallow water along shore. It commonly drags around a whelk shell; into which it can retreat when alarmed.

Several other species of hermit crabs are commonly found along the coast, some of the larger ones in quite deep water.

REFERENCES

Butler, T. H. 1950. The Commercial Shrimps of British Columbia. Progress Reports, Pacific, No. 83, pp. 30–34.

Mackay, Donald C. G. 1942. The Pacific Edible Crab, *Cancer magister*. Fish. Res. Bd., Canada, Bull. No. 62.

Spencer, G. J. 1932. The Commercial Crab, *Cancer magister* Dana, in Clayoquot Sound, Vancouver Island. Bio. Board of Canada, Bull. No. 30.

Schmitt, Waldo L. 1921. The Marine Decapod Crustacea of California. Univ. of Calif., Publ. Zool., Vol. 23.

Stevens, Belle A. 1925. Hermit Crabs of Friday Harbor, Washington. Publ., Puget Sound Biol. Sta., Vol. 3, No. 68.

BARNACLES

Despite the fact that barnacles live in a limy shell ilke that of a mollusc, they are members of the crustacea and are therefore related to the crabs and shrimps. Young barnacles start off life resembling the swimming young of other crustacea, but by a series of moults they increase in size and change their form until they reach the settling stage. At this point they affix themselves to a solid object and proceed to build the shell of the adult form around their body. For the remainder of its life each barnacle remains fixed in this position, literally standing on its head and kicking food into its mouth with its feet.

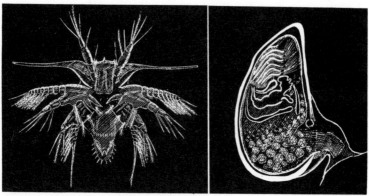

Two stages in the development of a barnacle: Left, a free-swimming larva; right, a newly attached individual.

Apart from certain parasitic species, there are two general types—acorn barnacles, which are attached directly to some support, and goose barnacles, which are attached by a flexible stalk or " neck."

Most common are the acorn barnacles, several species of which are abundant on rocks, boulders, and pilings between tide-levels. Some are capable of being exposed for many hours each day, feeding only when the tide covers them.

In the feeding process a hand-like structure, which is really made up of the feet, sweeps rhythmically through the water to gather minute plants, animals, or organic matter into the mouth. Periodically, as the animal grows, it casts off its old and now too-small skin before the new larger one hardens; when many cast at the same time, the water around wharves and floats may be filled with moulted skins complete with the hand-like sweep.

Acorn Barnacle   *Balanus cariosus* (Pallas)

One of the most numerous barnacles between high and low water. The shell varies exceedingly in appearance according to its environment. If uncrowded and not subject to erosion, the shell is cone-shaped and has a " thatched " appearance; if crowded and exposed to wave action, the shell is elongated and relatively smooth.

Colour white in young or uncrowded individuals; otherwise dirty grey.

Size up to 1¼ inches in diameter and 2½ inches in height.

Barnacles are a source of food for many marine animals. The swimming larval stages are eaten by small fishes and other plankton feeders, while the adults are preyed upon by whelks, starfishes, and possibly crabs. Larger species, such as the clouded barnacle (*Balanus nubilus*) found on kelp hold-fasts, were eaten by Indians after being roasted in the embers of a fire.

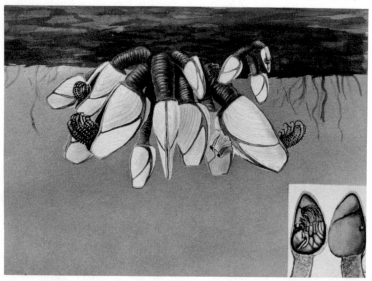

Goose Barnacle   *Lepas anatifera* **Linnæus**

A long-necked goose barnacle often attached to driftwood; body enclosed in five finely striated plates. Colour of plates dirty white or bluish-grey, edges of opening bright scarlet; stalk purplish-brown. Size of shelled portion up to 1¾ inches in length; stalk up to 8 inches in length, usually much shorter.

This barnacle is world-wide in distribution and is the species which gave rise to the ancient myth that barnacle geese arose from them. Several related species of stalked barnacles also occur on this coast; one, *Mitella polymerus,* is common in rock crevices and similar habitats, usually where there is some surf action.

All goose barnacles are edible, particularly those with a well-developed stalk. The stalk or " neck " is severed from the shell, steamed for twenty minutes and skinned; the flesh is pinkish-red in colour and reminiscent of shrimp or lobster in taste.

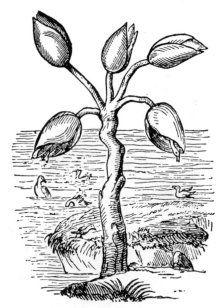

The barnacle tree (from Gerard's " Herball," 1597).

References

Cornwall, Ira E. 1955. The Barnacles of British Columbia. B.C. Prov. Museum Handbook No. 7, pp. 1–69.

Cornwall, Ira E. 1955. Arthropoda 10e Cirripedia (Barnacles). Fish. Res. Bd., Canada, Can. Pac. Fauna, No. 10, pp. 1–49.

Guberlet, Muriel Lewin. 1936. Animals of the Seashore. Binfords & Mort, Portland, Ore.

Quayle, D. B. 1952. The Myth of the Barnacle Goose. Victoria Naturalist, Vol. 9, No. 2, pp. 15–18.

MOLLUSCS

Most molluscs have a limy shell of some kind, but some, such as sea slugs, land slugs, and octopuses, do not. However, all have a soft body, a foot (used in locomotion), and a mantle (which forms the shell when present).

The shell is a permanent structure; it is not shed as in the crustaceans. As the animal grows, more material is added at intervals to the outer edge of the shell, with the result that a series of ridges or rings of growth is produced, by which the age of the mollusc may sometimes be determined.

Fishery regulations or officials should be consulted regarding closed seasons and other restrictions to digging clams or taking other molluscs.

Blue Mussel   *Mytilus edulis* **Linnæus**

A small mussel growing in masses below half-tide level.

Shell pointed at front end, rounded at the rear. Surface smooth, except for fine concentric ridges.

Colour black, blue, or brown; usually blue where outer layer is worn off.

Size up to 2 inches in length.

The blue mussel prefers quiet water, where it may be found in great numbers attached by thread-like structures to rocks, boulders, piles, and floats. It is edible and quite acceptable if taken from water uncontaminated by sewage.

A larger species, the California mussel (*Mytilus californianus*), which grows to 10 inches in length, is found on the open coastline. It is also edible, but can cause paralytic shell-fish poisoning at certain times.

A third kind, the horse mussel (*Modiolus rectus*), up to 8 inches long, grows solitary in sand, gravel, or mud.

Butter Clam　　　　　*Saxidomus giganteus* (**Deshayes**)

A medium-sized clam with heavy, strongly ridged shell.

Shells broadly oval in outline with a prominent hinge ligament.

Colour yellowish in young; greyish-white in adults.

Size up to 5 inches in length.

The butter clam is one of the most abundant molluscs in British Columbia and is the main support of the clam-digging industry. It was also one of the chief food items of coastal Indians in the past, judging by the great numbers of shells found in middens at many points along the shoreline.

It spawns in the summer months. The resulting larvæ swim for a period of time before settling, possibly some distance from the point of origin.

Little-neck Clams   *Protothaca staminea* (Conrad)
Venerupis japonica (Deshayes)

A small clam with a rounded, sculptured shell. Striations on shell both radiating and concentric. Three diverging teeth in hinge.

Colour of *Protothaca* white, sometimes with brown and white checks; *Venerupis* grey-brown or with black and white geometric pattern, yellow inside with purple at posterior end of shell.

Size of shell up to 2½ inches in length.

The native little-neck clam (*Protothaca*) is harvested commercially for the fresh market but is less important than the Manilla clam (*Venerupis*), which is now well established in British Columbia.

The Manilla clam or Japanese little-neck was first noted in 1936, probably having arrived with seed oysters from Japan. Since then it has become more abundant than the native species and is now widespread in Georgia Strait and at other localities along the coast.

Soft-shell Clam; Mud Clam   *Mya arenaria* **Linnæus**

A large clam with an easily broken shell. Front end rounded; rear end pointed. Surface with uneven concentric ridges. Left shell with a prominent internal lip at the hinge.

121

Colour white or grey, sometimes with a thin brownish or yellow covering at the edges.

Size of shell up to 6 inches in length.

Originally a native of the Atlantic Coast, where it is very plentiful, the soft-shell clam first appeared in the San Francisco Bay area, from which point it has spread northward partly by transplanting and partly by natural distribution. It is now common in the Georgia Gulf area and northward as far as the Queen Charlotte Islands.

Pacific Oyster   **Crassostrea gigas (Thunberg)**

A large oyster, often with a much-fluted shell but sometimes quite smooth. Shape irregular, depending on environment. Lower or left valve usually cupped; upper or right valve flatter and smaller.

Colour of shell grey or white; new growth often black or purple.

Size up to 12 inches in length, average about 5 or 6 when 3 years old.

The Pacific oyster was originally imported from Japan as "seed" oysters and planted in various parts along the Pacific coast. Seed is still imported to stock local beds, though this is not absolutely necessary as natural spawning takes place fairly regularly. In recent years Pacific oysters have become widely spread along the east coast of Vancouver Island as a result of several successful spawning seasons, and it has been planted elsewhere in large numbers.

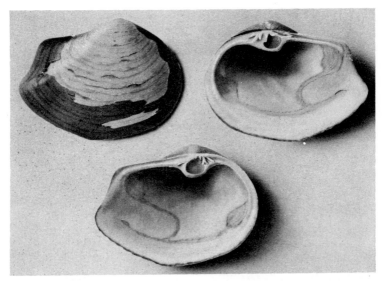

Horse Clam   *Schizothaerus capax* **(Gould)**

A large heavy-bodied clam with a long leathery neck. Outline of shell more or less rounded; shells gaping at posterior end. Hinge well toward the front end.

Colour white or yellowish with brown or black patchy outer covering.

Size of shell up to 8 inches in length and to 6 inches high; the neck may be 12 or more inches long.

The horse clam is one of the largest bivalves in British Columbia, second only to the geoduck in size. The empty shells are often found cast up on the beach, but the whole animal is seen only after a diligent search followed by laborious digging because it lives at some depth near the lowest tide-level.

Only the tip of the neck (siphon) shows above the surface of the sand or mud. It may be identified by its dark green or black colour, by the presence of horny pads on the tips, and by the tentacles fringing the inner edge of the opening.

Geoduck *Panope generosa* **Gould**

A very large heavy-bodied clam with a long leathery neck. Outline of shell more or less rectangular; shells gaping except at the hinge area. Hinge about midway between front and rear.

Colour grey-white with yellowish outer covering.

Size of shell up to 9 inches in length; neck often more than 12 inches long and capable of extension.

The geoduck is the largest clam on the Pacific Coast. It lives at the lowest tide-levels in muddy sand of protected bays and sometimes is up to 3 feet below the surface. All these factors combine to make it difficult to locate and to dig this clam, which is fortunate since it never was abundant.

Cockle   *Clinocardium nuttalli* (**Conrad**)

A clam with a rounded, heavy shell with prominent radiating ribs.

Colour drab grey with a thin brownish-yellow covering; chalky inside.

Size of shell up to 4½ inches in length.

The cockle, sometimes called basket cockle or heart cockle, is often found exposed on tide-flats among eel-grass. It moves by the vigorous action of a long muscular foot and may dig a shallow trench. While it is not abundant, it is considered to be excellent food.

125

Dog Whelk; Oyster Drill   *Thais lamellosus* (Gmelin)

A medium-sized snail with a wrinkled shell. Shell with 9 to 20 thin plates, elevated at the edge and extended where they meet a large spiral ridge. An operculum or plug blocks the opening when the snail is withdrawn.

Colour of shell white to brown through various shades of yellow, sometimes banded.

Size up to 4 inches or more in length.

Whelks of several species are sometimes abundant on sheltered rocky shores, where they feed on barnacles, clams, and other molluscs. Some obtain their meal by drilling a hole through the shell of the victim with a rasp-like tongue; others are apparently able to overcome their prey, especially barnacles, by means of a narcotizing agent which renders the victim helpless.

Whelks lay their eggs in capsules which resemble grains of oats attached to some solid support. They are sometimes called " sea oats."

Leather Chiton; Sea Cradle *Katharina tunicata* Wood

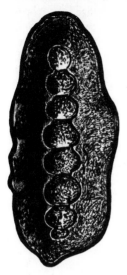

A medium-sized elongate snail with 8 plates on the back bordered by leathery skin. Plates overlapping and each about two-thirds covered by the tough, smooth mantle. Large foot on underside with mouth at front end. No tentacles or eyes.

Colour of exposed shell brown; girdle or mantle black; foot pale orange.

Size up to 3½ inches in length.

Chitons are a primitive type of snail, in which the shell is represented by 8 separate plates which overlap like shingles. When removed from the rock to which they are usually found clinging, chitons roll up armadillo-like into a shape which suggests the name " sea cradle."

References

Abbott, R. Tucker. 1954. American Sea shells. D. Van Nostrand Co., Inc., Toronto.

Quayle, D. B. 1941. The Edible Mulluscs of British Columbia. B.C. Commissioner of Fisheries Rept. for 1940, pp. 75–87.

Quayle, D. B. 1941. The Japanese " Little-neck " Clam Accidentally Introduced into British Columbia Waters. Fish. Res. Bd., Canada, Prog. Rept. (Pacific), No. 48, pp. 17–18.

Quayle, D. B. 1960. The Intertidal Bivalves of British Columbia. B.C. Prov. Museum Handbook No. 17, pp. 1–104.

SEA WORMS

Most members of this group are readily recognized as worms because they have the typically long body divided by constrictions into numerous segments, each one usually with a pair of legs. However, those that live in protective cases are not always easily identified as worms because the plume-like structures protruding from the cases are most unworm-like in appearance, suggesting other types of animals or even plants in their general appearance. Nevertheless, if removed from its cover the body shows all the characteristics of the true worms.

The true worms (as distinct from flat worms, round worms, ribbon worms, etc.) are represented by many species in British Columbia, and their identification requires the services of an expert. Two common forms only are included in this booklet.

Pile Worm

Nereis vexillosa Grube

A typical worm with an elongate body divided into more than 100 segments; each segment behind the head provided with a pair of paddle-like feet.

The most common colour is an iridescent greenish-brown.

Size from 2 to 8 inches in length.

The pile worm is one of the most abundant and widespread marine animals on the coast. It may be found almost anywhere — under rocks, beneath clumps of mussels, in loose gravel, or wherever shelter is provided. When picked up it may evert the pharynx, which is armed with formidable-looking teeth capable of inflicting a painful bite.

In the spawning season the male's posterior half, containing the sexual products, is green, while the female's is red. When tide and moon phase are favourable, the colourful worms emerge from hiding and swim rapidly through the water near the surface, where they shed the sperms and eggs. At these times the worms may be attracted in large numbers to a light hung over the water, where one may witness a spectacular show of speeding worms. darting in all directions.

Plume Worm

Eudistylia vancouveri (**Kinberg**)

A worm living in a parchment-like tube and having flower-like tentacles.

Tube almost any length up to 18 inches, of tough leathery material, largely concealed in rock crevice or among rocks. Tentacles displayed like petals of a delicate flower, up to 2½ inches in diameter.

Colour of tentacles maroon with transverse bands of dark green. Tube dark brown.

The plume worm, sometimes called " tube worm " or " umbrella worm," may be found anywhere among rocks near the low-tide level. When in water the expanded gill filaments attract attention because of their graceful shape and attractive colours. A light touch or even a passing shadow may cause the worm to retract the gills quickly into the tube out of sight. Besides carrying on respiration, the filaments assist in the gathering of food.

Many other species of tube worms may be found at low tide. Some build shelters of sand grains, some of bits of shell and small stones, and some construct solid limy tubes cemented securely to rock or similar support. Worms in tubes of the latter type often have bright red gills and a " stopper " with which to plug the entrance-way.

REFERENCES

Berkeley, E. and C. 1948. Annelida 9 b(1) Polychæta Errantia. (Free-living worms). Fish. Res. Bd., Canada, Can. Pac. Fauna, No. 9, pp. 1–100.

Berkeley, E. and C. 1952. Annelida 9 b(2) Polychæta Sedentaria (Tube-living worms). Fish. Res. Bd., Canada, Can. Pac. Fauna, No. 9, pp. 1–139.

Guberlet, Muriel Lewin. 1936. Animals of the Seashore. Binfords & Mort.

WOOD BORERS

Two marine animals burrow into wood — the pin-worm or gribble and the shipworm or teredo. The first named is a small crustacean, a relative of the sowbug and pillbug (isopod) which attacks the outside surface of wood; the shipworm is a mollusc (a bivalve like the clam) which destroys from the inside. Both are serious pests, being destructive of logs in booms, piles, ships' hulls, and any other structure of unprotected wood in salt water.

Gribble   *Limnoria lignorum* (Rathke)

A small crustacean, shaped like a miniature sowbug, in a shallow burrow on the surface of wood.

Size about three-sixteenths of an inch in length.

The gribble, sometimes known as " pin-worm " by boat-owners, attacks wood by channelling a shallow burrow usually in the direction of the grain. As the roof of the tunnel flakes away, new burrows are started or the old ones are deepened so that the outer surface of the wood is rapidly destroyed.

Eggs are carried in a brood pouch on the underside of the female. The young, when hatched, are ready to begin eating wood immediately, usually near the parent. Thus a colony is constantly spreading.

Although wood may be attacked at any time of the year, it is most open to gribble infestation in late winter and early spring. Copper painting or storage programmes should be planned with this in mind.

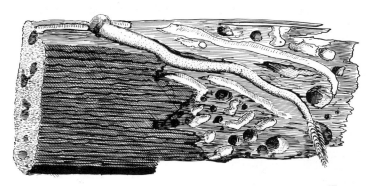

Shipworm   *Bankia setacea* **Tryon**

A long worm-like soft-bodied animal enclosed in wood, with two small shells at the head-end and a feather-shaped structure at the tail-end.

Colour of shells, feather-like structures (pallets), and most of the body white; remainder translucent.

Size up to 3 feet in length and three-quarters of an inch in diameter.

The shipworm is a bivalve mollusc, a member of the same group to which belong the clam and the oyster. The shells in this animal, however, are designed for rasping wood, and with them the shipworm bores through wooden structures, using part of the "sawdust" so produced as food.

The young begin life as small swimming larvæ which seek out wood, into which they enter by boring a minute hole. Once inside they continue to burrow, usually following the grain and usually laying down a thin lining of shelly material. If many shipworms are present, they can completely destroy the wood in a relatively short time.

Wooden structures can be protected from gribble and shipworm attack in several ways—by the use of creosoted lumber, by coating with anti-fouling paint, or by a sheathing of copper or plastic. None

133

is effective if a break occurs in the protective covering. Underwater explosions and certain chemical poisons are sometimes used to give temporary protection to log booms and wharf pilings.

The shipworm is commonly called " teredo," a name which originates from the Atlantic species which belongs to the genus *Teredo*.

REFERENCES

Neave, S. L. 1960 Gribble Attack on Wood Immersed in Sea Water. Prov. Museum Rept. for 1959, pp. 32–39.

Quayle, D. B. 1955. The British Columbia Shipworm. B.C. Dept. of Fisheries Rept., 1955.

Caddy, the Sea Serpent *Cadborosaurus* (Wills)

A serpent-like creature said to have an elongated neck and several coils or humps along the back. Head reported to be camel-like, with or without mane; mouth usually with teeth. Total length variable, depending upon circumstances or condition of observer.

Habitat: Coastal area of southern Vancouver Island.

Status and relationship: Questionable.

Type locality: Cadboro Bay, after which it was named by Mr. Archie Wills, of Victoria, B.C.

134

APPENDIX

How to Make Kelp Pickle

Ingredients

4 cups of rings or rectangles cut from fresh stems of kelp (*Nereocystis*).

¾ cup white vinegar.

2½ cups sugar.

1 tablespoon mixed pickling spice.

1 teaspoon whole cloves.

Method

Remove the outer skin of kelp stem with a vegetable-peeler and slice into thin rings or cut into longitudinal strips and then into rectangles. Soak the cut kelp in fresh water for three days, changing the water several times a day to remove the bitter-tasting salts.

Enclose the spices in a cheesecloth bag and place in simmering vinegar and sugar for five minutes. Remove spices and pour the hot syrup over the sliced kelp. Let stand overnight.

Next day drain off syrup, heat to boiling, and pour over kelp again; let stand overnight.

On the following day (sixth) remove syrup and heat to boiling. Place kelp slices in hot jars, cover with boiling syrup, and seal, or store the pickled kelp in a covered crock.

How to Preserve Starfishes and Sea Urchins

Starfishes and sea urchins are best preserved by drying after "fixing" them in a preserving fluid. First, place the specimens in a container of sea-water containing commercial formalin in the ratio of about one part of formalin to ten parts of water and leave them to soak at least overnight, but preferably several days. Then remove and dry them, preferably in the shade or over a source of heat and where no one will object to the smell!

Soft-bodied forms will shrink somewhat in the process, and all will lose their bright colours to some extent. However, colour can often be restored by painting after the specimen has become thoroughly dry.

BRITISH COLUMBIA PROVINCIAL MUSEUM PUBLICATIONS

(Prices Subject to Change Without Notice)

NOTE—Handbooks Nos. 1 and 4 have been replaced with Handbooks Nos. 20 and 24 respectively.

SYESIS

An annual journal directed toward professionals and dealing with studies of the Pacific Northwest, particularly the natural and human history of British Columbia. The annual subscription is $5.

Publications may go out of print from time to time, therefore purchasers should inquire about the status of a particular publication before placing their order.

Please address orders and inquiries to:

PUBLICATIONS
British Columbia Provincial Museum
Victoria, B.C. V8W 1X4

Make cheques or money orders payable to the Minister of Finance, Province of British Columbia.